REALITY:

Scientific and Spiritual

With insight and rare objectivity, Professor John C. Greene shows how Darwinism has brought about a slowly changing attitude on the part of both Catholics and Protestants who have held a literal and static acceptance of Biblical revelation. Many Christians now regard the Bible as a human record of divine disclosure, inspired, but subject to human distortion throughout the ages.

Despite scrutiny by sympathetic and hostile scholars, the Bible has survived, although evolution is recognized as scientific reality. Modern man now accepts Darwin's scientific philosophy so completely that he seldom questions it . . . however, as Professor Greene points out, Darwin's influence has resulted in some modern ills: Darwin emphasized individual, racial, and national competition as a source of social progress; he believed that science could support itself without philosophy or religion. In this unusual book, Professor Greene convincingly argues that scientific truth cannot be meaningful when it denies the reality of the spirit— human or divine.

MENTOR Books of Related Interest

The Death of Adam *by John C. Greene*

A study of the impact of the theory of evolution on Western thought.   (#MT339—75¢)

The Origin of Species *by Charles Darwin*
                              Introduction by Sir Julian Huxley

The classic work on man's evolution, that revolutionized scientific and religious thinking from the 19th century onwards.   (#MT294—75¢)

The Future of Man *by P. B. Medawar*

An inquiry into the fitness of the human race and its potential for further evolution.

(#MD331—50¢)

On the Nature of Man *by John Langdon Davies*

A lucid examination of the nature of man—both physical and psychological—stressing the devastating impact of modern science on time-worn beliefs and assumptions.   (#MD334—50¢)

To Our Readers: If your dealer does not have the Signet and Mentor books you want, you may order them by mail enclosing the list price plus 5¢ a copy to cover mailing. If you would like our free catalog, please request it by postcard. The New American Library of World Literature, Inc., P. O. Box 2310, Grand Central Station, New York 17, N. Y.

DARWIN
and the
MODERN
WORLD VIEW

The Rockwell Lectures, Rice University

by

JOHN C. GREENE

 A MENTOR BOOK

Published by THE NEW AMERICAN LIBRARY

215
G811

For
Bert James Loewenberg
teacher, scholar, friend

Preface

THIS LITTLE BOOK PRESENTS THE SUBSTANCE OF THREE
lectures on Darwin and modern thought delivered at
Rice University in the spring of 1960 in the Rockwell
Lecture series. The first two chapters deal with Darwin's
influence on Christian thought; the third examines his role
in modern social theory, especially the theory of social
evolution. Obviously, these topics do not exhaust the
subject of Darwin's intellectual influence, nor can they
be treated as extensively as they deserve in so brief a
compass. The most I can hope to do is to indicate the
range and general tendency of the intellectual response
to Darwin, leaving it to the reader to explore special topics
more fully. Those interested in the rise and influence of
evolutionary ideas before Darwin may wish to consult
my *The Death of Adam: Evolution and Its Impact on
Western Thought*.

I owe an enormous debt of gratitude to the many
scholars who assisted me in preparing these lectures for
publication by giving me the benefit of their advice and
criticism. The views of some of these scholars are expounded in this book, but I alone am responsible for
the exposition, except where I have quoted their own
words. Among Catholic scholars I would mention especially Father David M. Stanley, S.J.; Father Raymond J.
Nogar, O.P.; Father James A. Weisheipl, O.P.; Father
John Collins, S.J.; Professor James Collins of St. Louis

University; and Professor J. R. E. Ramirez of Duquesne University. For criticism from the Protestant point of view, I am indebted to Professors Jaroslav Pelikan, J. V. Langmead Casserley, and Emerson Shideler. Among my scientific friends, Professors Theodosius Dobzhansky, Irving Goldman, Murray Wax, A. Irving Hallowell, Walter Rothenbuhler, Joseph O'Mara, Gerhard Tintner, Walter Hearn, and Philip Leis have been especially helpful. In matters of style I have benefited greatly from the suggestions of Mrs. Rowena James.

To Professor Bert James Loewenberg, a lifelong student of Darwin and his influence, I owe much more than acknowledgment of his assistance in connection with this book. It was he who first awakened my interest in intellectual history, who persuaded Harvard University to grant me a scholarship for graduate study, and who turned my thoughts toward Darwin and his role in modern thought. Throughout the years he has been a loyal friend and stimulating critic. I cannot hope that he will agree with all of the opinions expressed in these pages, nor perhaps even with my general point of view, but I know that he would be the first to bid me take my stand.

Lastly, I am deeply grateful to President and Mrs. William V. Houston, Dean William H. Masterson and his colleagues, and my old friend Martin Ettlinger for their gracious hospitality during my stay at Rice University. They made my first visit to Houston an extremely pleasant one.

JOHN C. GREENE

Iowa State University
of Science and Technology
March 6, 1961

Contents

1

Darwin and the Bible

O F ALL HISTORIES THE HISTORY OF IDEAS IS THE MOST difficult and elusive. Unlike things, ideas cannot be handled, weighed, and measured. They exert a powerful force in human history, but a force difficult to estimate. When we attempt to describe Darwin's influence on modern thought, we soon find how hard it is to disentangle his effect from the innumerable other influences that have shaped its course and from the influence exerted by Western ideas on Darwin himself. Western thought is all of a piece, an organic growth of scientific, religious, and philosophical ideas mutually interacting. In Darwin's day the impact of natural science on philosophy and religion was more spectacular than their return effect on scientific ideas. Indeed, it was so spectacular that some thinkers predicted the early extinction of theology and metaphysics and a general triumph of modes of thought derived from natural science. Darwin himself felt the pull of this incoming tide of positivistic naturalism. It shows up in his *Origin of Species* and *The Descent of Man* alongside more traditional attitudes and ideas. These books, in turn, reinforced the intellectual tendency of the times, raising and sharpening issues concerning nature, man, and God that still challenge us.

11

In our first two chapters we shall be concerned with the effect of Darwin's writings on Christian thought. We shall greatly exaggerate his influence, however, unless we view it in proper perspective, against the background of the historical development of the conflict between science and religion in modern times. We may divide this development, for purposes of analysis, into three overlapping stages. In the first stage, the triumphs of Newtonian science gave rise to deism as a rival of Christianity and precipitated the eighteenth century debate between the advocates of natural religion and the defenders of Christianity as a revealed religion. Darwin was to play an important part with respect to belief in the inspiration of Scripture, but it is important to realize that the Bible's claim to constitute a unique and infallible revelation from God had been challenged vigorously long before Darwin appeared on the scene.

In the second stage of conflict, a stage which reached a climax in Darwin's day, the progress of astronomy, geology, and paleontology undermined the static view of nature that had been taken for granted by both Christians and deists and stimulated the growth of evolutionary ideas in both natural and social science. In this development Darwin played a last-minute but decisive role; he convinced the scientific world that the whole array of nature's species had evolved from simpler forms during vast periods of time.

In the third stage, the stage in which we ourselves are now caught up, the methods of natural science were extended to the study of man and society, and the claim was advanced in some quarters that these methods constituted man's only reliable access to knowledge of reality. As we shall see, Darwin gave a powerful impetus to the social sciences and to these far-reaching claims for the all-sufficiency of scientific method.

To recapitulate in slightly different terms, we may say that the challenge to belief in the inspiration and inerrancy of the Bible was uppermost in the first stage of the modern conflict between science and religion, the challenge to the doctrine of creation dominated the second stage, and the issue concerning the adequacy of scientific methods in the study of man and society has become crucial in our own day. Obviously, these stages overlap each other. The debate concerning Scripture did not stop when the evolutionary challenge to the static view of nature came to the fore. Nor did the issue concerning the doctrine of creation disappear when the claims of social science demanded attention. All three phases of the conflict are still very much with us, the intensity of each phase varying in different regions of the country and on different educational levels. Darwin was not the sole, or even the chief, cause of the debates which raged, and still rage, around these issues, but his writings have been of major importance in them. A study of his influence may help to clarify our own search for a lasting accommodation between science and religion.

Our first task is to examine the effect of Darwin's writings on belief in the divine inspiration of the Bible. As we have indicated, this doctrine had been under attack for more than a century before Darwin took up his pen to begin work on the *Origin of Species*. Newtonian science had undermined belief in the inspiration of the Bible in two ways. On the one hand, it gave rise to a mechanical philosophy in which nature was conceived as a law-bound system of matter in motion, every state of the system proceeding from previous states by mathematical rule. This view was totally incompatible with the Hebrew concept of nature, in which events were referred immediately to the will of God, and the line between ordinary and miraculous events was very thin. On the other hand, the progress of science and technology enhanced the prestige of human reason and intoxicated men with the hope that society was capable of indefinite progress in this world if only individuals could be freed from institutional restraints and allowed to pursue happiness in their own way. To those who shared this faith—men like Thomas Jefferson and Benjamin Franklin —Christian emphasis on the sinfulness of human nature and the need for redemption by divine grace, Christian preoccupation with the world to come, and Christian

theological disputation all seemed obstacles in the way
of human progress. Redemption was something which
would take place here and now by man's own efforts in
history. As for revelations, nature and its laws were a
sufficient revelation of the Creator, exhibiting His wisdom, omnipotence, and benevolence. In Tom Paine's
view, the solar system was a lecture room so arranged by
the Almighty Lecturer that the inhabitants of each planet
could discover the laws of motion by observing the motions of other planets about the sun. In his book *The Age
of Reason,* subtitled *True Theology Distinguished from
False,* Paine compared the claims of the Bible to constitute
a divine revelation with those of nature. The Bible, he
wrote, is man-made; nature is the handiwork of God. The
Bible has suffered innumerable alterations and corrup-
tions through copying, revision, and translation; nature exists indestructibly in her pristine perfection. The
Bible presents God as a passionate, vindictive, changeable
being; nature displays Him as immutable and benevolent.
The Bible ascribes to God an earlier and a later revelation; nature displays one eternal revelation. The biblical
revelation appeared late in history and to one nation
only; the revelation in nature is proclaimed to all peoples
from the beginning of time. Scripture is based on the testimony of human witnesses; God's word in nature is written in blazing characters of light, that he who runs may
read. The Bible condones atrocities; nature teaches man
to emulate the benevolence of his Maker. The Bible envelops truth in mystery; the truths of nature are clear
and compelling to human reason. In the Bible, God com-
municates with man by magical hocus-pocus; in nature
He speaks to man through his ordinary senses. Theology
is the study of human opinions concerning God; science
is the investigation of the divine laws which govern nature.

Thus Paine's argument ran. The astonishing thing about
it from the modern point of view, apart from Paine's
total insensitivity to the spiritual profundity of the Bible,
is his confident assumption that nature unambiguously
discloses an omnipotent, omniscient, and benevolent
Creator who cares enough about man to provide him

with natural faculties sufficient for working out his own salvation unaided. Events were to show that nature makes no such unambiguous disclosure and that Paine's confidence that it did was derived, not from the study of nature, but from the natural theology of his day. Deism, or natural religion, was compounded of two not entirely compatible elements: first, the idea of nature as a law-bound system of matter in motion, and, second, the idea of nature as a framework of permanent structures divinely contrived and adapted as a stage for the activities of intelligent beings. The latter idea came to the deists straight from Christian natural theology. The former was derived from Newtonian science. In the long run the Newtonian concept was to prove fatal to *any* static conception of nature, whether Christian or deist, for it implied the mutability of all of the visible structures of nature. Darwin's theory of evolution was as fatal to deism as it was to Archdeacon William Paley's natural theology, for both rested on a static version of the doctrine of creation.

Thus matters stood in the western world about the time that Charles Darwin went to Cambridge University to study for the ministry, having already disappointed his father's hopes of making a physician of him. At this time Darwin was a conforming though not an especially devout Anglican, apparently untroubled by the issues raised in the eighteenth century debate between the attackers and defenders of Christianity. As a student, he read with admiration Archdeacon Paley's closely argued *View of the Evidences of Christianity,* in which Paley undertook to prove the divine origin of the Bible, and hence of Christianity, from the miraculous and historically well-authenticated character of the events recorded in its pages. According to Darwin's own testimony, it was not until after his return from the epoch-making voyage of the *Beagle* that he began seriously to examine the grounds of Christian faith and, having tried them, found them wanting. His account of this ordeal, written nearly half a century later, is sufficiently interesting and revealing to merit quotation at length:

. . . I had gradually come, by this time, to see that the Old Testament from its manifestly false history of the world and from its attributing to God the feelings of a revengeful tyrant, was no more to be trusted than the sacred books of the Hindoos, or the beliefs of any barbarian. The question then continually rose before my mind and would not be banished,—is it credible that if God were now to make a revelation to the Hindoos, would he permit it to be connected with the belief in Vishnu, Siva, &c, as Christianity is connected with the Old Testament. This appeared to me utterly incredible.

By further reflecting that the clearest evidence would be requisite to make any sane man believe in the miracles by which Christianity is supported,—that the more we know of the fixed laws of nature the more incredible do miracles become,—that the men at that time were ignorant and credulous to a degree almost incomprehensible by us,—that the Gospels cannot be proved to have been written simultaneously with the events,—that they differ in many important details, far too important as it seemed to me to be admitted as the usual inaccuracies of eyewitnesses;—by such reflections as these, which I give not as having the least novelty or value, but as they influenced me, I gradually came to disbelieve in Christianity as a divine revelation. . . . This disbelief crept over me at a very slow rate, but was at last complete. The rate was so slow that I felt no distress, and have never since doubted even for a single second that my conclusion was correct.[1]

As Darwin himself concedes, there was nothing especially new or original in his examination of the issue. The arguments which convinced him had influenced deists and free thinkers for more than a century, from the time of Chubb and Bolingbroke to that of Paine and Hume. One wonders, however, whether Darwin may not have left something out of the story, either deliberately or by lapse of memory. The years 1836–1838 in which he examined the claims of Christianity were precisely the years in which he conceived his theory of organic evolution. This theory, he observed in a notebook dated 1837, would affect the whole of metaphysics. He did not say so, but it would affect the whole of religion too. If this were true, what was its influence on the outcome of Darwin's reflections on the Bible? Was his conclusion that the history of the world in the Old Testament was "manifestly false" unaffected by the new and staggering view of man's ancestry at which he had already arrived, though he did not profess it publicly until *The Descent of Man?* Was his rejection of Paley's *View of the Evidences of Christianity* entirely unrelated to his discovery that Paley's equally famous *Natural Theology* was rendered dubious by the theory of natural selection? If an argument as old and tried as the argument from design could prove doubtful, could not the close reasoning of the *Evidences* prove equally unconvincing?

Whatever Darwin's own thoughts may have been, there can be no question that his influence on other peoples' attitudes toward the Bible sprang primarily from the doubt he cast on the historical authenticity of the Scriptural account of human origins. As we shall see, Darwin was by no means the first to suggest that man had evolved slowly from a brutish condition. But he was the first to convert the scientific world to this point of view and thus to transform a disturbing speculation into a settled scientific theory that could not be ignored or brushed aside. If Darwin was right about man's origin, and the scientific community increasingly inclined to the view that he was, the doctrine of the inspiration and total inerrancy of Scripture would have to be re-examined, perhaps discarded. It was in helping to force a reconsideration of traditional doctrines concerning revelation and inspiration that Darwin played a decisive role with respect to the Bible.

Belief in the divine inspiration of the Bible is as old as Christianity itself, the author of the Second Epistle to Timothy declaring that "all Scripture is given by the inspiration of God." The Church Fathers elaborated this belief into doctrine and drew from it the corollary of the absolute infallibility of the Bible. "The Lord's words

are true; for Him to say it, means that it is," wrote Saint
Jerome. The same doctrine recurs in the pronouncements
of the Roman Catholic Church throughout the centuries—
in the decrees of the Council of Trent in the sixteenth
century, in those of the Vatican Council in 1870, in Pope
Leo XIII's encyclical *Providentissimus Deus* of 1893,
and in more recent pronouncements.

> For all the books which the Church receives as sacred
> and canonical [says Leo XIII] are written wholly and
> entirely, with all their parts, at the dictation of the Holy
> Spirit; and so far is it from being possible that any
> error can coexist with inspiration, that inspiration not
> only is essentially incompatible with error, but excludes
> and rejects it as absolutely and necessarily as it is im-
> possible that God Himself the supreme Truth, can utter
> that which is not true.[2]

Much the same attitude prevailed in Protestant circles. Appealing to the Bible against the authority of the
Roman Church, the Reformers were not inclined to doubt
either the divine inspiration or the absolute inerrancy of
Scripture. A nineteenth century Protestant definition of
inspiration as consisting in "such divine influence upon
the minds of the sacred writers as rendered them exempt
from error, both in regard to the ideas and the words" is
not substantially different from Leo XIII's dictum that
God so assisted the sacred authors "that the things which
He ordered, and those only, they first rightly understood,
then willed faithfully to write down, and finally expressed
in apt words and with infallible truth." [3]

It should be stressed, however, that inspiration thus
defined did not require a literal interpretation of the
Bible. The Church Fathers never hesitated to resort to
allegorical interpretation when a literal rendering seemed
insufficient. Saint Augustine's rule of interpretation—"not
to depart from the literal and obvious sense, except only
where reason makes it untenable or necessity requires"—
was the general rule of both Protestants and Catholics.
Thus, in the nineteenth century the six days of creation
were frequently interpreted as six periods of indefinite

length. Behind the innumerable reconciliations of science and the Bible lay the firm conviction that whatever Scripture said on any subject was, when properly interpreted, substantially true. God's truth revealed in His word could not conflict with God's truth revealed in His works. It seemed to scientists and clergymen alike as long as the views we have been describing prevailed that if the two revelations appeared to clash, the discrepancy must arise from some error either in science or in biblical exegesis. Thus, Matthew F. Maury, founder of the science of oceanography, laid it down as a rule of conduct:

> . . . never to forget who is the Author of the great volume which nature spreads out before us, & always to remember that the same Being is also the Author of the book which Revelation holds up to us; & though the two works are entirely different, their records are equally true; & when they bear upon the same point . . . it is as impossible that they should contradict each other as it is that either should contradict itself. If the two cannot be reconciled, the fault is ours, & it is because, in our blindness & weakness, we have not been able to interpret aright, either the one or the other or both.[4]

The vehemence of the religious reaction to Darwin's *Origin of Species* and his *The Descent of Man* cannot be understood apart from the challenge they presented to the doctrine of biblical inspiration. Three quarters of a century earlier Tom Paine's attack on Scriptural infallibility in *The Age of Reason* had provoked a similar reaction. "What!" exclaimed Bishop Richard Watson in his famous reply to Paine:

> . . . is it a story then, that the world had a beginning, and that the author of it was God? . . . Is it a story, that our first parents fell from a paradisiacal state— that this earth was destroyed by a deluge—that Noah and his family were preserved in the ark—and that the world has been repeopled by his descendants?—Look into a book so common that almost everybody has it,

and so excellent that no person ought to be without it—
Grotius on the truth of the Christian religion—and you
will there meet with abundant testimony [from profane
history] to the truth of all the principal facts recorded
in Genesis. . . . The oldest book in the world is Genesis;
and it is remarkable that those books which come
nearest to it in age, are those which make, either the
most distinct mention, or the most evident allusion to
the facts related in Genesis . . .[5]

A similar cry of outraged indignation greeted Darwin's
The Descent of Man. The point was not simply that
human dignity seemed to be impugned by Darwin's theory
of man's origin, although that was injury enough. Worse
yet, the whole doctrine of inspiration, with its comforting
assurance that everything man needed to know about his
origin, duty, and destiny had been divulged by God Himself, was shaken to its very foundations. The great theological doctrines of creation and fall, sin and redemption,
with all the moral precepts hanging on them, seemed
threatened by a preposterous theory that man was a cousin to the apes, if not of closer consanguinity.

That the doctrine of biblical inspiration was the sore
point is shown by the public outcry in 1860, one year
after Darwin's *Origin of Species,* against a book, *Essays
and Reviews,* in which several eminent Anglican clergymen and scholars (among them the renowned translator
of Plato, Benjamin Jowett) attempted to apply ordinary
methods of historical inquiry and literary criticism to the
Bible.

The essayists [writes H. G. Wood] were soon involved
in a storm of ecclesiastical censure. They were violently
attacked in the Quarterly Review. An episcopal letter
condemning all the essays without much qualification
or discrimination was . . . signed by most of the leading
bishops . . . Two of the essayists . . . were put on trial
for heresy and, though they were acquitted on appeal,
both Houses of Convocation passed resolutions re-
affirming their condemnation of the book . . . It was
quite clear that the older conception of inspiration,

which Christians shared with Jewish writers like Philo and Josephus, was no longer tenable. But it was very hard for Christians to surrender a point of view so deeply ingrained, which seemed indispensable for the maintenance of the authority of the Bible.[6]

With unerring polemical instinct, Thomas Henry Huxley saw that belief in the inspiration and inerrancy of the Bible was a chief bulwark of opposition to Darwin's theory of evolution and to the spread of confidence in the adequacy of scientific methods. Against the doctrine of inspiration he marshalled all the arguments at his command, drawing from geology and paleontology, from biology and anthropology, and from biblical criticism. By 1893 he felt that the victory had largely been won. "For 'plenary inspiration,' " he wrote, "we are asked to substitute a sort of 'inspiration with limited liability,' the limit being susceptible of indefinite fluctuation in correspondence with the demands of scientific criticism. This Parthian policy is carried out with some dexterity; but, like other such maneuvers in the face of a strong foe, it seems likely to end in disaster." [7]

The doctrine of inspiration was indeed on the defensive, but the issue concerning the revelatory character of Scripture had by no means been settled. The response of Christian faith to the combined challenge of evolutionary biology, comparative religion, and biblical scholarship was varied and complex. It still goes on.

In the Roman Catholic Church the initial reaction to Darwinism was a vigorous reaffirmation of the inspiration and absolute inerrancy of the Bible. But this reaffirmation was not occasioned by Darwinism alone. It was merely one facet of the Church's struggle with modernist ideas generally. After two centuries of intellectual and institutional decline, Roman Catholicism had begun to revive. Turning its back on modernism and secularism in the decrees of the Vatican Council of 1870, the Church returned to its ancient moorings in patristic and scholastic theology. Encouraged by Leo XIII (1878–1903), Thomistic theology and Catholic biblical scholarship began a spectacular resurgence. The intellectual life of the Church was reviving, but under close control from Rome. In 1895 the Holy Office condemned a book on evolution by Father Eduard Leroy; in the following year a similar work by an American Catholic, Father John Zahm of Notre Dame University, was withdrawn from circulation. In 1902 a Pontifical Biblical Commission was established to supervise the progress of biblical studies in the Church. The Commission instructed Catholic exegetes to maintain the "substantial authenticity" and "Mosaic integrity" of the Pentateuch and directed that whatever was asserted, enunciated, or suggested by the authors of Scripture must be held to be asserted, enunciated, or suggested by the Holy Spirit. It frowned on the idea that the Apostles, though not teaching any error, could nevertheless express erroneous personal and human ideas while under the inspiration of the Holy Spirit.

The effect of these and other stringent measures against modernism was to delay the Church's accommodation to evolutionary biology and biblical scholarship. They produced a defensive atmosphere in which creative scholarship was difficult. "For twenty to thirty years," writes a modern Catholic theologian, "no Catholic scholar dared to touch such books as Genesis, Josue, Judges or Isaias. Consequently Scripture courses in our seminaries and colleges usually degenerated into unyielding conservatism and prolonged arguments against the higher critics." [8]

This situation could not continue indefinitely. Within the Church itself scholars and scientists began to urge a redefinition of the old doctrines to make room for the results of modern research. "Is it not desirable that theologians take up the problems of their contemporaries, instead of basking lazily in the tranquil possession of the truth?" asked one of these critics. "What exactly did God reveal?" asked another. "Did he reveal that the body of man came *directly* from the dust, or is this a human interpretation? The doubts of those of us who believe will vanish if we are given the true meaning of the word of God, and we will go on in the certainty that science, which today is uncertain, will tomorrow shed light on the origin of the human body *in harmony with the divine word*. But if the theologians do not yet know the true meaning of the revelation, let them not impose upon us a burden which many may not be able to bear." [9]

These criticisms were not without effect. In his encyclical *Divino Afflante Spiritu,* issued in 1943 in commemoration of the fiftieth anniversary of *Providentissimus Deus,* Pope Pius XII called attention to the enormous progress made in archaeology and biblical studies since the time of Leo XIII. These researches, he said, had thrown new light on the nature and effects of biblical inspiration. They had made it plain that something more than philological and grammatical learning was needed to interpret the meaning of Scripture. The interpreter, said Pius XII, must "go back wholly in spirit to those remote centuries of the East and with the aid of history, archaeology, ethnology, and other sciences, accurately determine what modes of writing . . . the authors of that ancient period would be likely to use, and in fact did use."

> . . . no one, who has a correct idea of biblical inspiration, will be surprised to find, even in the Sacred Writers, as in other ancient authors, certain fixed ways of expounding and narrating, certain definite idioms, especially of a kind peculiar to the Semitic tongues, so-called approximations, and certain hyperbolical modes of expression, nay, at times, even paradoxical, which even help to impress the ideas more deeply on the mind. For of the modes of expression which, among ancient peoples, and especially those of the East, human language used to express its thought, none is excluded from the Sacred Books, provided the way of speaking adopted in no wise contradicts the holiness and truth of God. . . . For as the substantial Word of God became like to men in all things, "except sin," so the words of God, expressed in human language, are made like to human speech in every respect, except error.[10]

The bearing of Pius XII's pronouncements on the interpretation of Genesis was elucidated at some length in a response of the Biblical Commission in 1948. Referring to its earlier responses on this subject, the Commission indicated that these should not be construed as preventing a re-examination of problems of scriptural interpretation in the light of forty years' progress in research. It was no longer disputed, said the Commission, that Moses made use of oral traditions and written documents in composing his narrative or that the Mosaic laws had undergone a progressive development in response to changing social and religious conditions. Whereas the Commission had exacted strict maintenance of the "substantial authenticity" and "Mosaic integrity" of the Pentateuch in 1906, it was content in 1948 to observe that the scholarly research it invited would "doubtless establish the great part and deep influence exercised by Moses both as author and lawgiver." [11]

With respect to evolutionary biology, too, the Church showed an accommodating spirit. In his encyclical *Humani Generis* issued in 1951, Pope Pius XII declared that the teaching authority of the Church did not forbid that:

. . . in conformity with the present state of science and theology, the doctrine of evolution should be examined and discussed by experts in both fields, in so far as it deals with research on the origin of the human body, which it states to come from pre-existent organic matter (the Catholic faith obliges us to believe that souls were created directly by God). But this must be done in such a way that the arguments of the two opinions, that is, the one favorable and the other contrary to evolution, should be weighed and judged with all necessary seriousness, moderation, and restraint, and on condition that they are all ready to submit to the judgment of the Church, to which Christ has entrusted the office of interpreting authentically the Holy Scriptures and of defending the dogmas of the faith.[12]

Catholic scholars and theologians have not been slow to make use of the greater freedom allowed by these recent decrees. In the field of biblical scholarship there has been a remarkable outburst of Catholic activity. Catholic attendance at international congresses of biblical scholars has increased markedly. Catholic biblical journals now rival Protestant journals of the same kind in number and quality, and Catholic translations of the Bible are appearing on every side. At the same time the doctrine of inspiration is being carefully re-examined in the light of new discoveries and ideas. An "incarnational" concept of biblical inspiration is coming into favor among Catholic interpreters. "Inspiration," says Dom Celestin Charlier, "is . . . infinitely more than the communication by God of a kind of mechanical influx which subordinates to it the literary activity of certain free instruments; it is the productive, all-embracing penetration, by the Holy Spirit's vivifying action, of the whole history of the people of God." [13] The Bible, adds Father David M. Stanley, is *Heilsgeschichte,* salvation history, in which the divine and human elements are inextricably mingled.

> Since the Bible as salvation-history is *primarily* God's self-revelation, God must be regarded as principal Author of Scripture. At the same time, and of necessity, the Bible, written by men, is an epiphany of those men's response of loving obedience and faith to God's message. . . . For the human author is not a mere secretary; nor can he be, if God's aim is to be achieved. In consequence, the hagiographer must contribute something of his own; not merely his individual way of expressing the divine word (his *genus litterarium*), but also his own faith's response to God's message. The Bible is accordingly, *at one and the same time,* God's self-revelation and that of the inspired writer. While these two are to be distinguished, they must not be divided up materially, as if, for instance, Jesus' words in the Gospels are the divine element and the evangelist's remarks the human. The entire narrative is necessarily a divine-human word.[14]

The interpretation of this divine-human document requires sympathetic understanding of the genius of Semitic culture, its spiritual outlook, its idea of truth, its

concept of authorship, and its literary methods, Father
Stanley explains. To the authors of Scripture, truth was
not a body of abstract doctrine arrived at by philosophical
inquiry. It was something experienced in a personal encounter with the living God. It was something revealed
in history, the personal histories of the sacred authors
and the history of their nation. Their purpose in writing,
therefore, was not to communicate abstract truths in the
Greek manner but to declare the mighty acts God had
performed and would perform. It was to exhort men to live
the truth that had been made manifest.

What this shift from a purely critical to a theological,
or psychological, interpretation of Scripture means with
respect to practical issues, such as evolution, may be seen
in recent Roman Catholic publications. One has only to
look at Father Bruce Vawter's *A Path Through Genesis,*
Father John MacKenzie's *The Two-Edged Sword,* or at
Father Charles Hauret's book on the first five chapters of
Genesis, entitled *Beginnings: Genesis and Modern Science,*
to appreciate the extent to which the doctrine of
the inerrancy of Scripture, though still formally asserted, has been modified in application. The book by
Father Hauret, a member of the Theological Faculty of the
University of Strasbourg, was translated into English at the
suggestion of a professor of biology at Saint Ambrose
College in Davenport, Iowa, having previously met with
a favorable reception in France, Spain, and Italy. Let us
see how Genesis is interpreted in this work.

Father Hauret begins by accepting the conclusion of
geologists and paleontologists that our universe was in
process of formation during millions of years. The author
of Genesis, says Father Hauret, was not interested in the
duration or particular circumstances of cosmic evolution.
His sole purpose was to convey the message that the
universe was created by God. The details of his narrative
were determined by his religious purpose and his literary
technique, not by his scientific understanding. The framework of six days, for example, was dictated by literary
convenience rather than by historical reality. The order
of events is logical, not chronological, "a deliberate and

artistic disposition of his materials which in no way affects
the underlying historical reality affirmed by the sacred
writer, the fact of creation by God." Father Hauret does
not deny that there may be some similarity between the
order of events pictured in Scripture and that worked out
by geologists, but he regards such agreement, if it exists,
as purely coincidental. "We can admit this harmony, if
there be one, but we are not proposing any form of
concordism." A far cry this from nineteenth century efforts to demonstrate the perfect concordance of Genesis and geology! At the same time Father Hauret, faithful
to the dictates of the Church, holds that the sacred author
"neither errs nor leads us into error."

> Under the inspiration of the Holy Spirit [he writes]
> the sacred author simply expressed himself in accordance
> with his own primitive theories. He was not writing in
> order to propose, assert, or imply his "scientific no-
> tions"; the interests of a science teacher were not his
> interests. But his deep-seated hidden opinions, things
> taken for granted, so colored his language that we can
> divine or guess what his personal convictions were.
> Between what he deliberately intends to say . . . and
> what he may privately think about a certain subject
> there may be a vast difference—a significant difference
> for our interpretation of Sacred Scripture, for the in-
> spired author's private opinions are not guaranteed by
> God but only his deliberate, intended, "official" pro-
> nouncements. Thus, on reading the first chapter of
> Genesis we can perceive the scientific notions of the
> author; they are, by the way, erroneous. He shares
> them with his contemporaries, but properly speaking he
> does not express them, does not affirm them, nor is it
> his intention to imply them.[15]

Father Hauret is equally free in his interpretation of the
biblical account of the origin and development of life on
the earth. The purpose of the sacred author, he explains,
was to declare that all living beings derive their existence
from God. As to how life first began on earth and how it
subsequently developed, whether by evolution or other-

wise, the author of Genesis "asserts nothing." "There is
. . . nothing in favor of and nothing against the theory of
the transformation of species." Since neither Saint
Gregory of Nyssa nor Saint Augustine regarded the idea of
an initial creation of all beings in their present forms as
part of the deposit of faith, why should modern theologians
and exegetes feel constrained to adopt such a position?
"More and more Catholics, some of them university
professors," writes Father Hauret, "have come out openly
for a spiritualistic, teleological, theistic transformism. Nor
are their ideas confined to the initiated, for they successively win over their own students and the Catholic elite,
and then penetrate little by little into the popular mind." [16]

The biblical accounts of man's creation have given
Catholic scholars more difficulty than the passages describing the creation of the world. Interpretations range
all the way from the creation of man's body directly
from inorganic matter to the gradual development of
the human body by a series of sudden, divinely directed
mutations, at the last of which God created and infused a
human soul into the organism thus prepared. All of these
theories, Father Hauret observes, safeguard the idea of the
special creation of man, yet none of them is entirely convincing or satisfactory. As in the case of the creation of
the world, the biblical author seems more interested in
who created man than in *how* he was created.

On the question of woman's origin, Father Hauret continues, the scriptural account is highly circumstantial,
and exegesis has been constrained severely by the response of the Biblical Commission in 1915 citing this
narrative as one closely related to fundamental Christian teachings; hence not to be questioned as to its literal
and historical meaning. This response has made evolutionary interpretation difficult but has not precluded it altogether. Mutations have been invoked by some, symbolic
interpretations by others. Some writers suggest that God
used Adam's body in forming Eve's only in the sense that
the first woman was modelled after the first man; others
regard the story as a kind of parable which yet points to
a historical reality. Thus, the exact manner of woman's

creation remains undecided. The Biblical Commission has recently declared that it is not opposed to further discussion of the subject in the light of modern research, but until its earlier response is formally modified, the Catholic scholar is bound to respect it, although he may, says Father Hauret, "honestly point out the difficulties which he feels modern science encounters in following what he may think to be an outmoded directive."

Some idea of the long and difficult struggle which has taken place in the Church with respect to evolution, more especially human evolution, may be gained from the *Souvenirs* published in 1945 by Count Henri Begouën, a French Catholic anthropologist and prehistorian.[17] As Count Begouën makes clear, there were evolutionists in the Church from the beginning of the Darwinian controversy, but their lot was a hard one until recent times. As late as 1925 there was a concerted effort among the conservatives to discredit evolutionists like Canon Henri de Dorlodot and Father Teilhard de Chardin and to prevail upon the Holy Office to publish a general condemnation of evolutionary doctrines. Throughout Europe Catholic evolutionists took steps to prevent this. In the summer of 1925 a distinguished group of them assembled in connection with the excavations in progress at the famous cave of Altamira in the Pyrenees. After four days of discussion they decided to submit a memoir to Pope Pius XI to forestall the maneuvers of their "integrist" adversaries. The Pope's response through the papal nuncio at Paris was reassuring. No condemnation of evolutionary theory was issued. Tension relaxed. Eighteen years later the aging Count Begouën had the satisfaction of reading the encyclical *Divino Afflante Spiritu,* the harbinger of a new epoch in biblical interpretation.

In summary, we may say that the doctrine of scriptural inspiration and inerrancy, though still formally maintained by the Roman Catholic Church, has undergone considerable reinterpretation in response to the pressure of modern science and scholarship. It is conceded that the Bible contains erroneous conceptions, but these are held to be the private, incidental, and "unofficial" opinions or assumptions of the human authors of Scripture, not opinions they intended to assert or imply, much less the opinions of the Holy Spirit. Inerrancy is claimed only for the meaning the inspired writer intended to convey. Novel as such views may seem in comparison with those which prevailed in Darwin's time, Catholic scholars insist that, far from being new, they represent a revival and development of principles of interpretation laid down by the Church Fathers. Exegetes recognize, however, that the limitation of inerrancy to the meaning intended by the sacred author may result in "a serious lack of certitude concerning the truth of Sacred Scripture," since scholars sometimes disagree in assessing the intention of the biblical writers. For Catholics, however, this incertitude is removed whenever the Church, "the guardian and *only* authentic interpreter of Sacred Scripture," declares the true meaning of the passages in question.[18] Belief in the inspiration and inerrancy of the Bible is thus closely linked to belief in the infallibility of the Church.

In the Protestant world, where there is no central authority competent to declare the true meaning of Scripture, the response to modern science and scholarship has necessarily been more diverse than in Roman Catholic circles. In the United States it took the form of a long drawn out controversy between fundamentalists and modernists, a controversy that reached a spectacular climax in the Scopes trial in 1925. Among the modernists the doctrine of absolute inerrancy was abandoned in favor of ideas of progressive revelation. Scripture came to be regarded as the record *par excellence* of man's enduring search for religious and moral truth. In Lyman Abbott's *Theology of an Evolutionist*, published in 1897, the Bible was viewed as "a collection of literature, containing in a pre-eminent measure the growth of the consciousness of God in the human soul, as interpreted by the pre-eminent religious leaders of a pre-eminently religious people." [19] The authors of the Bible, said Abbott, were not divine amanuenses transcribing a supernatural message. Their relation to God was more like that of a chemistry student to a wise teacher who, instead of proclaiming the truths of science from the lecture platform, inspires his pupil to discover them for himself by observation and experiment. Like the chemistry student, the sacred authors apprehended truth gradually and imperfectly. Infallibility and inerrancy were no more to be expected of them than of the scientist in his laboratory. Revelation was not something handed down from above, once and for all. It was a progressive human discovery of moral and spiritual truth under divine tutelage and inspiration. In that process of discovery, said Abbott, the writers of the Bible played a pre-eminent role, a role probably never to be surpassed. But although they were lifted above ordinary men in power of perception and expression, they by no means transcended the limitations of human nature. In science and philosophy they were children of their time and race. In the spiritual realm their genius lay in formulating, purifying, and extending man's growing understanding of God, an understanding infinitely enriched by God's revelation of Himself in the life, death, and resurrection of Jesus Christ. Revelation did not cease with them, but their moral and spiritual insight was as unlikely to be transcended by later generations as were the literary achievements of Homer, Sophocles, and Shakespeare.

Thus Lyman Abbott argued, making revelation itself an evolutionary development. The fundamentalists would have none of this. Instead, they reacted to the challenge of new ideas with a vehement reaffirmation of plenary inspiration in its narrowest, most literal, form. Whatever could not be squared with the plain sense of Scripture must be rejected root and branch. But even fundamentalism has not been as monolithic and impervious to change as most people think. Many conservative Protestant groups adhering to some idea of verbal inspiration resent the name "fundamentalist" and seek to distinguish themselves from those whom they call "hyper-orthodox" or "hypertraditionalists." These "conservative Christians," as they prefer to be called, include many able scientists in their ranks. A group of these scientists, known as the American Scientific Affiliation, recently published a volume of essays

entitled *Evolution and Christian Thought Today* under
the editorship of Russell L. Mixter, Professor of Zoology
at Wheaton College in Illinois. The essays display substantial scientific erudition and a wide variety of opinion
with respect to evolution and its bearing on the Bible. In
the opinion of George K. Schweitzer, Associate Professor of Chemistry at the University of Tennessee, the
biblical account of the creation of the universe was intended to tell us who created the universe not how it
was created. Modern research, he declares, has shown that
the early chapters of Genesis are not to be interpreted
literally, but "poetically or allegorically." So interpreted,
he finds them compatible with either the superdense-state
theory of the origin of the universe expounded by the
astrophysicist George Gamow or with the steady-state
theory favored by Fred Hoyle and others.

The Bible is vague and figurative with respect to the
origin of life, say Professors Walter Hearn and Richard
Hendry, biochemists at Iowa State University and West-
minster College respectively, in their contribution to this
same book. In their view, Scripture places little or no
limitation on possible mechanisms for the origin of life. It
leaves the Christian free to choose among current scientific hypotheses, not excepting those which envisage
the origin of life from inanimate matter through the operation of known physico-chemical processes. Hearn and
Hendry declare that if Christians are unwilling to entertain
such hypotheses, at least provisionally, there is bound to
be conflict on this point.

The chapter on genetics in this book is equally learned
and open-minded. Without taking sides definitively, the
authors lean to the view that the geneticist is engaged in
studying the process of creation. Why should God act
differently in creating than He does in sustaining the universe? If His *modus operandi* has remained unchanged, it
may be possible for scientists to describe His creative
activity. "Viewed in this light, the discoveries in genetics
may be nothing more than such a scientific description."

Next come several chapters on species, their origin,
distribution, crossing, and extinction. The authors of these

chapters, though not in harmony on all points, seem to agree that the scientific facts indicate considerable evolution of new types on a limited scale and that the phrase in Genesis about each plant and animal reproducing "after its kind" is not to be taken as asserting the fixity of species. The term "kind" is presumed to have a much broader reference, possibly to orders rather than species. Hence the real issue is not whether new species have originated by ordinary processes in the course of nature's history but whether *all* existing species have developed from one or a few very simple types of organisms. Even on the latter question "conservative Christians" are not in general agreement. Although most of them incline to creationist views, some believe that God directs evolutionary processes much as a chess player directs his chessmen. "This view," we are told, "is growing rapidly today, and is taught largely in church-related schools as well as from many pulpits, and in many public schools in communities with a strong religious background. Various degrees of it are found in the writings of . . . such thoroughly orthodox theologians as A. H. Strong and James Orr, and others who also consider the Bible and evolution to be mutually consistent." [20]

A creationist view of modern anthropology closes the scientific part of the book we have been discussing. The author, Professor James O. Buswell III of Wheaton College, finds no difficulty in granting an antiquity of hundreds of thousands of years to mankind or in conceding that early men may have been somewhat pithecoid in appearance. For, says Buswell, "although the creationist . . . must of necessity hold to the belief . . . that there was a 'first man,' it is of no consequence whether he looked like a Pithecanthropoid or a Caucasoid. Furthermore, if anthropological opinion swings in favor of calling some prehistoric types by separate specific or generic names, and calls other types *Homo sapiens* with modern man, this is of relatively little consequence. For the creationist recognizes the arbitrary and non-qualitative nature of taxonomic categories and is not bound to equate any one of them with the 'kind' spoken of in Genesis 1." [21] But

Buswell himself is not willing to grant the evolution of man's body from lower forms of life. He finds this repugnant both on anthropological and on theological grounds, especially because it clashes with the doctrine of the original perfection and subsequent fall of man. In this respect, Buswell is more conservative than many of his anthropological colleagues in the Catholic Church.

It appears, then, that "fundamentalist" opposition to biological evolution, though still narrowly dogmatic in many quarters, has undergone considerable change and modification in others. The verbal inspiration of Scripture is still maintained, but interpretation within this framework allows for a limited amount of organic development and even for a general evolutionism in some cases. Generally speaking, however, these Protestants adhere to some kind of special creation theory. Some interpret the six days of creation as geologic ages, some regard them as ordinary days separated by vast intervening periods, and some restrict the application of the creation account to the locality of the Garden of Eden. These theories may help to conserve belief in the inspiration of the Bible, but it is difficult to see how they can be of much scientific value, if the value of a scientific theory is to be judged by its suggestiveness in indicating new avenues for research. As science advances, moreover, the maintenance of what these writers call "verbal inspiration" is likely to prove possible only by continual reinterpretation of the Bible. In the long run, perpetual reinterpretation may prove more subversive of the authority of Scripture than would a frank recognition of the limitations of traditional doctrines.

Although the modernist-fundamentalist controversy dominated the American religious scene for half a century after Darwin's death, it would be a mistake to regard it as exhausting the Protestant reaction to the growth of modern knowledge. It would be equally erroneous to imagine that the development of religious ideas has been a simple reflex of scientific progress. Both modernism and fundamentalism took as their starting point a rather mechanical conception of inspiration that had taken hold in

the eighteenth and early nineteenth centuries, but this
view of inspiration had not always prevailed. In Martin
Luther's view, his biographer Roland Bainton tells us,
Jesus Christ was the Word of God.

> This Word brought Scripture into being. Scripture it-
> self is not the Word. Scripture is the manger in which
> lies the Babe, the Word. But Scripture is infinitely
> precious because it is the record of the Word. Scripture
> as the cradle of the Word provides a norm by which to
> judge the Church.
>   At the same time, the Word within Scripture may be
> used to judge Scripture. Luther treated Scripture with
> amazing freedom, with so much freedom indeed that
> one wonders why he did not disrupt the canon.[22]

In the eighteenth and nineteenth centuries there was
a general decline of theology and a corresponding im-
poverishment of concepts of inspiration and revelation.
The rethinking of these concepts in our own day is but
one aspect of the modern revival of theology, the
causes of which lie deeper than science and scholarship,
however great an influence we assign to them. At any
rate, we need not be surprised to find modern theologians and exegetes returning to the great theological ages
of the past for guidance in reconsidering traditional
doctrines concerning the Bible.

Such a process of rethinking—one that has gained
momentum in such diverse camps as Anglicanism, neo-
orthodoxy, and post-modernist liberalism—is described
and analyzed in John Baillie's book *The Idea of Revelation in Recent Thought*. The central idea which Baill-
lie finds emerging in these Protestant circles is that
revelation is not a body of propositions supernaturally
communicated, but rather a series of events in which God
disclosed Himself by His action in history. The Bible,
then, is a human record and interpretation of those events,
divinely inspired in the sense that God illuminated the
minds of the authors of Scripture, enabling them to re-
spond to His self-disclosure in the events, but thoroughly
human in that this illumination did not overcome the

limitations of finite, historically-conditioned minds and temperaments. The revelation in the events was refracted, one might say, by the human medium through which it was transmitted. Hence, although Scripture manifests the Word of God, it is not itself that Word. "There is no such thing as revealed truth," writes Archbishop William Temple, an eminent Anglican spokesman for this point of view. "There are truths of revelation; but they are not themselves directly revealed." [23] Karl Barth, prophet and herald of neo-orthodoxy, puts the same idea in a somewhat different way:

> Revelation has to do with the Jesus Christ who was to come and who finally, when the time was fulfilled, did come—and so with the actual, literal Word spoken now really and directly by God Himself. In the Bible we have to do in all cases with human attempts to repeat and reproduce this Word of God in human thoughts and human words with reference to particular human situations, e.g. in regard to . . . the errors and confusions of the Christian congregation in Corinth between A.D. 50 and 60. In the one case *Deus dixit,* but in the other *Paulus dixit;* and these are two different things.[24]

A strong note of historical relativism pervades much of this modern writing on revelation. The Bible is held to be revelatory only for those who approach it from the standpoint of faith. When the Church speaks of revelation, says Helmut Richard Niebuhr in *The Meaning of Revelation,* "it never means simply the Scriptures, but only Scriptures read from the point of view and in the context of church history." The history in which revelation occurs is the internal history of the Christian community, history as felt and lived rather than history as viewed by a detached observer. The revelatory event occurs in external history, but it becomes revelatory only in the context of internal history, the inner history of the Christian community. It is revelatory because it makes sense of that history, enabling the believer to discern the meaning of his personal and communal existence. It appeals to the practical rather than the speculative reason, disclosing relationships between persons rather than things.

> The heart must reason; the participating self cannot escape the necessity of looking for pattern and meaning in its life and relations. It cannot make a choice between reason and imagination but only between reasoning on the basis of adequate images and thinking with the aid of evil imaginations. Neither the primitive images of animism nor the impersonal patterns of modern scientific, or indeed of any kind of purely contemplative, thought supply a basis for the rational understanding of the self in its community and history. But there is an image neither evil nor inadequate which enables the heart to understand, and the event through which that image is given them Christians call their revelation.[25]

If this is the meaning of revelation, what is meant by "inspiration"? Inspiration, says Baillie, is the divine illumination that enables the human mind to grasp and interpret the divine self-disclosure. But was this illumination of such a character in the case of the authors of Scripture as to remove all possibility of error and to guarantee the accuracy and adequacy of the Scriptural witness? Yes, say the advocates of plenary inspiration, whether Protestant or Roman Catholic. No, say the modern Protestants whose view of revelation we have just presented. The doctrine of biblical inerrancy, says Archbishop Temple, sprang from a craving for final and unquestionable authority in religious matters. But the Bible can provide such authority only if there is an infallible Church to interpret Scripture and an infallible Pope or Council to speak for the infallible Church. Such a solution is clearly unacceptable to Protestants. They have no infallible Church, no infallible spokesman, and, on this view of revelation, no infallible Bible. For them, the divine self-disclosure is apprehended by faith, not faith in the sense of assent to a body of doctrine and information supernaturally revealed, but faith in the saving power of the great event which climaxed God's revelation of Himself.

All this may seem far removed from Charles Darwin, the *Origin of Species,* and *The Descent of Man,* but the distance is not so great as it may seem. Darwin was not indispensable to the rethinking of traditional ideas concerning revelation and inspiration that has taken place since his time. Biblical scholarship would have brought it about eventually quite apart from his influence. But Darwin does seem to have played the role of a catalytic agent, helping to precipitate the reaction. The challenge he presented to continued belief in the historicity of Genesis was too grave to be ignored. Adam and Eve taken literally could not be reconciled with *The Descent of Man;* something had to give. Generally speaking, it has been the doctrine of absolute inerrancy that has yielded, rapidly in some quarters, slowly, grudgingly, and covertly in others, but inevitably in all. Yet, strangely enough, Scripture seems to have weathered the ordeal remarkably well. Scholars have pored over every page, every line, every word of it. Controversy has raged around it with inexhaustible fury. Yet the Bible survives and still proclaims its message with power and eloquence. Its authors thought they had seen and heard the living God and had been commissioned to speak in His name. Their claim is as challenging today as it was nearly two thousand years ago, and the human response to that claim is as varied and poignant now as it was then. At a recent conference of scholars in New York City, the Bible was the topic for much learned discussion by eminent archaeologists, biblical scholars, and historians. These experts were as divided in their attitude toward Scripture as their audience was. The line of division did not run between Catholic, Protestant, and Jew, however. Instead, it ran between those who found in the pages of Scripture a revelation of God and those who did not. The discussion was erudite and spirited, but inconclusive. Nor is this surprising. Science and scholarship may influence conceptions of revelation and inspiration, but they cannot resolve the question whether the Bible is in truth what believers say it is, a record of God's self-disclosure in history.

2
Darwin and Natural Theology

NATURAL THEOLOGY IS A SUBJECT SELDOM MEN-
tioned nowadays. Many people have little idea what
the term means. In Darwin's time, however, it was in
high vogue; Darwin acknowledged its influence on his
own thinking. Yet the natural theology Darwin knew was
but a remnant of the rich tradition that took its rise in
Greek philosophy and found consummate expression in
St. Thomas Aquinas' five proofs of the existence of God.
St. Thomas distinguished clearly between theological
truths accessible to human reason (such as God's existence and attributes) and those accessible only by revelation (such as the Incarnation and the Trinity). In his
view, there were five mutually supporting ways by which
men could arrive at a knowledge of God and His attributes by natural reason. The first proof was based on
the necessity of a Prime Mover to account for the movement evident in the universe, the second on the need
for a First Efficient Cause of the existence of things,
the third on the need to postulate a Necessary Being in a
world of contingent beings, the fourth on the need to
presuppose a Supremely Perfect Being as the cause of
the degrees of perfection observable in things, and the

fifth on the necessity of a Supreme Intelligence as the cause of the order prevailing in the universe.

In subsequent centuries natural theology was first weakened, then transformed. Preaching the radical corruption of human nature at the Fall, Martin Luther and John Calvin flatly denied the power of unregenerate reason to rise unassisted to a knowledge of God and his attributes. Natural theology suffered a sharp decline. With the rise and progress of modern science, however, confidence in human reason reawakened, and physicotheology, a special variant of the argument from design, rapidly gained favor. Set forth in treatises such as John Ray's *The Wisdom of God Manifested in the Works of the Creation* (1691), physicotheology stressed the adaptation of structure to function throughout nature, regarding it as wisely ordained by an omnipotent Creator from the first creation of things. This attitude, in turn, was part of a wider set of presuppositions implicit in the static version of the doctrine of creation. The works of creation, said John Ray, a great biologist as well as a clergyman, were "the Works created by God at first, and by him conserved to this Day in the same State and Condition in which they were first made." All of the basic structures of nature—stars, solar systems, mountains, oceans, species—were regarded as permanent and wisely contrived. From this point of view, natural science was not concerned with explaining the origin of things. Its task was rather to name, classify, and describe; to investigate the uses of things; to discover natural systems like the solar system and display their wise design. Thus, Newton found in the fact that all of the planets and their satellites rotated and revolved in the same direction and in approximately the same plane a convincing demonstration that the solar system had issued directly from the hand of God. "For it became who created them to set them in order. And if he did so, it's unphilosophical to seek for any other Origin of the World, or to pretend that it might arise out of a Chaos by the mere laws of Nature . . ." [1] It was physicotheology of this kind that Darwin became acquainted with through William Paley's

Natural Theology (1802), in which the admirable adaptation of structure to function in plants and animals was compared to the cunning contrivance of spring and gears in a watch.

This conviction of the permanence and wise design of the fundamental structures of nature was gradually undermined in the eighteenth and nineteenth centuries, as evidences of natural mutability accumulated and the implications of the mechanical view of nature slowly became apparent. In astronomy the speculative temptation to derive the earth and the solar system from a previous state of the system of matter in motion by the operation of mechanical laws produced the nebular hypothesis, outlined by Immanuel Kant in 1755 and elaborated by Pierre Simon Laplace and William Herschel in the early nineteenth century. Simultaneously the nascent sciences of geology and paleontology were uncovering evidence of perpetual change on the surface of the earth. With the publication of Georges Cuvier's researches on fossil quadrupeds in the first decade of the nineteenth century, it could no longer be doubted that many species of animals had become extinct. The static view of nature was tottering, but the implication of universal mutability was evaded for a long time by a compromise theory postulating successive creations separated by geological upheavals. This theory made it possible to admit the fact of change in nature without admitting development, that is, without conceding that change was fundamental and structure transient and superficial. It also turned aside the disturbing idea that changes on the inorganic level set the pace for changes on the organic level instead of organism and environment being adapted to each other in a pre-established harmony. There was, however, a school of "uniformitarian" geologists, including James Hutton of Edinburgh and (somewhat later) Charles Lyell, who insisted that all the present appearances on the surface of the earth must be explained in terms of geological processes still in operation and, consequently, that millions and millions of years must have been required to form the present earth out of the ruins of earlier worlds. To this process of geological change Hutton could see "no vestige of a beginning, no prospect of an end." From similar premises the French biologist Jean Lamarck drew the inevitable conclusion that biological species were subject to constant slow change; otherwise they could not remain adapted to the changing environment. According to Lamarck, plants and animals faced with new situations made blind and groping efforts to survive. Organs that had once been useful became less useful and gradually withered away. Other organs became highly useful and developed rapidly from generation to generation. In extraordinary circumstances entirely new organs arose in response to the demands of environment. By these means, with the aid of "plenty of time and circumstances," the whole array of plants and animals had developed from the simplest beginnings.

By Darwin's time the static view of nature was in precarious condition. Darwin delivered the *coup de grace* by propounding a mechanism of organic change that seemed to eliminate the last trace of wise design in the formation of species. According to Lamarck, the modifications that enabled organisms to survive in a changing environment resulted from their efforts to survive. The animal that became a giraffe got its long neck by perpetually stretching to reach the leaves on the trees. In Darwin's theory, on the contrary, variations in neck length and a thousand other characters, springing from unknown causes, were perfectly random with respect to the needs of the organisms in which they occurred. Among these accidental variations some proved more useful in the competition for life than others. And since the amazing fecundity of plants and animals precipitated a perpetual struggle for food and living space, those individuals that happened to vary in a fortunate way would be most likely to survive and reproduce their kind. In the long run the average character of plant and animal populations in a given environment would change as, year after year, some lines of variation survived and multiplied and other lines diminished in numbers and eventually became extinct. On this view of things, the giraffe represented a line of animals that happened to vary in the direction of longer necks. Luck, not effort, accounted for their success. Thus, chance and struggle, the antitheses of design and pre-established harmony, became the architects of the adaptation from which natural theologians had argued the divine contrivance of nature. "The old argument of design in nature, as given by Paley, which formerly seemed to me so conclusive, fails, now that the law of natural selection has been discovered," Darwin wrote in his autobiography. "There seems to be no more design in the variability of organic beings and in the action of natural selection, than in the course which the wind blows. Everything in nature is the result of fixed laws." [2]

The deists, too, had believed that nature was governed by fixed laws. For them, however, law was the antithesis of chance. It operated to insure perfect stability in nature's basic structures and perfect equilibrium in her operations. It pointed clearly to a wise and omnipotent Lawgiver. But the law of natural selection was a new kind of law, a statistical law governing the chances of survival of randomly varying organisms in an overcrowded world. It was a law of trial and error, of adaptation through wholesale extinction, of survival by luck—a law of higglety-pigglety, the astronomer John Herschel protested. True, the fittest always survived. But who were the fittest? By definition they were those that survived. Survival was both the test and the outcome of fitness. There was no escaping the circularity of the argument, no way of proving any substantive excellence in what survived. Yet, strange to say, the competition for survival seemed to have produced a trend toward higher forms of life, something that looked like progress, however sporadic and piecemeal. Viewing the process as a whole, Darwin oscillated between admiration for its results and dismay at its brutal inefficiency. In his happier moods he could extol the superb workmanship of natural selection, "daily and hourly scrutinizing, throughout the world, every variation, even the slightest; rejecting that which is bad, preserving and adding up all that is good; silently and insensibly working, *whenever and*

wherever opportunity offers, at the improvement of each
organic being in relation to its organic and inorganic conditions of life." At other times, and increasingly as life
wore on, his thoughts took a gloomier turn.

> There seems to me too much misery in the world [Dar-
> win wrote to Asa Gray]. I cannot persuade myself that
> a beneficent and omnipotent God would have designedly
> created the Ichneumonidae with the express intention
> of their feeding within the living bodies of caterpillars,
> or that a cat should play with mice. Not believing this,
> I see no necessity in the belief that the eye was express-
> ly designed. On the other hand, I cannot anyhow be
> contented to view this wonderful universe, and espe-
> cially the nature of man, and to conclude that everything
> is the result of brute force. I am inclined to look at
> everything as resulting from designed laws, with the
> details, whether good or bad, left to the working out
> of what we may call chance. Not that this notion *at all*
> satisfies me. I feel most deeply that the whole subject is
> too profound for the human intellect. A dog might as
> well speculate on the mind of Newton. Let each man
> hope and believe what he can.[3]

For his own part, Darwin found himself able to believe
less and less as time went on. Having lost faith in God the
Judge and Redeemer in his early manhood, he felt his
belief in God the Creator slip slowly away from him in
his old age. For Darwin, natural theology was summed up
in William Paley's argument from design. When that
argument appeared to fail, Darwin was left without re-
source. He had, he confessed, "no head for metaphysics."
Science, not philosophy, was his business. He became an
agnostic.

Darwin's reflections on the meaning of evolution could
give little satisfaction to Christians facing the challenge of
his theory for the doctrine of creation. Those who rejected the theory of evolution had no problem, of course.
They could continue to think of creation and of natural
theology in the traditional way. But those who accepted
organic evolution as a fact of nature had to find a way of

reconciling it with Christian doctrine. One way was to regard the process of evolution as God's method of bringing about progress in nature and history. This view harmonized neatly with the optimistic faith in progress so common in the nineteenth and in the early twentieth century. It was a view difficult to reconcile with traditional doctrines concerning man's original perfection and subsequent fall from grace, but these doctrines were not very popular among modernist Christians anyway. They preferred to regard history as a redemptive process in which man evolved through higher and higher stages of culture, gradually sloughing off habits and attitudes inherited from an animal past. In this view of things, science was a chief instrument of progress. By tracing out the laws, mechanisms, and stages of evolutionary advance, it provided the basis for an evolutionary natural theology. Progress, not the wise adaptation of structure to function, became the proof of divine superintendence.

We can see the beginnings of this kind of theological adaptation to evolutionary biology in Henry Ward Beecher's sermon "The Two Revelations," preached from the pulpit of Plymouth Church on Sunday morning, May 31, 1885. In Beecher's day the phrase "the two revelations" usually meant the revelation in Scripture and the revelation in nature. But Beecher had little to say about the Bible in this sermon. The two revelations he had in mind were the revelation in nature and the revelation in history. The Bible, Beecher explained, tells us that God created the universe, but science must determine by what natural laws He accomplished this purpose.

> There are two records of God's creative energy. One is the record of the unfolding of *man* and of the race under the inspiration of God's nature: this is a mere sketch; of the ancient periods of man there is almost nothing known. The other of these records or revelations . . . pertains to the physical globe, and reveals the divine thought through the unfolding history of matter; and this is the older. So we have two revelations: God's thought in the evolution of matter, and God's thought in the evolution of mind; and these are the

Old Testament and the New—not in the usual sense of those terms, but in an appropriate scientific use of them. . . . If to reject God's revelation of the Book is infidelity, what is it to reject God's revelation of himself in the structure of the whole globe? [4]

Plainly Beecher was as confident that evolutionary science would provide a basis for natural theology as John Ray had been that the old natural history, based on the assumption of fixity in nature, would do so. In the evolutionary version of natural theology, however, the proofs of God's existence and attributes would be derived less from traces of design in nature's productions than from evidences of progress in her history. Now that nature was shown to have had a long and eventful history, the providence of God rather than His activity as Creator seemed the important thing to stress. Geological history was the process by which the earth had been prepared for man's habitation. Organic evolution was the process by which God had developed a creature, man, fit to inhabit such a world. Human history was but the latest chapter in the history of nature, the whole development being under providential direction. The old distinction between natural and revealed religion, natural and revealed theology, was all but erased. The Bible was but the most striking record of God's revelation of Himself in history.

The lengths to which such an optimistic natural theology based on wholehearted acceptance of evolution could be carried are shown in a book entitled *Contributions of Science to Religion,* edited by Shailer Mathews, Dean of the Divinity School of the University of Chicago, in 1924, a year before the Scopes trial. Mathews' basic idea in his contribution to this book was that all particular religions were phases of religion-in-general and that religion-in-general, conceived as a set of attitudes and activities whereby life adjusts itself to the environment, had undergone a progressive evolution toward higher and more complex forms.

Religion [Mathews wrote] is life functioning in the interest of self-protection. It differs from similar func-

tional expressions of life in that (1) it treats certain
elements of its environment personally (though not
necessarily as a person), by utilizing social practices and
ideas as forms of worship, or as patterns for beliefs,
and (2) it seeks to make these elements friendly and so
helpful. . . . The essential matter in the evolution of
religion as in all evolution is the transformation of the
original organism through its relation with its environment and the nucleating about itself . . . of the cells of
other experiences into species of the same genus.[5]

Here we see comparative religion blended with an evolutionary model of thought borrowed from biology; Christianity is regarded as a recent, highly-evolved species of
religion-in-general.

Mathews then proceeded to trace the states through
which religion had passed in its historical evolution. The
key to the whole development, he declared, was "the
struggle between religions for the survival of the fittest."
But what religion was fittest to survive? That religion,
answered Mathews, which was best adapted to the whole
cultural milieu in which it functioned.

What really will happen will be a biological development of religions through appropriation and assimila-
tion. . . . In other words, a nation will have several
religions, although they may be called by the same
general name and have many elements in common.
Some of these religions will be so unlike those of earlier
stages of social evolution as to constitute a new species.
In the struggle which comes between these various em-
bodiments of the religious impulse those elements will
disappear which are least in harmony with dominating
social conceptions of various social groups, and those
will survive which are most in accordance with and can
contribute most to the development of superior stages
of social evolution. . . . That religion which best enables
the religious impulse to express itself in its increasingly
complex social environment will survive all others.
Other religions will not altogether disappear, but they
will become vestiges in the more highly developed religious life. And, in this struggle of religions to express

religion, Christianity in its ethical and theological sense
is certain to be a dominant element.[6]

But what of revelation? What of the Bible and its
authority? Traditional theology, answered Mathews, started
with God as the existence revealed in Scripture and in
nature; it then proceeded to use biblical concepts in ex-
pounding Christian doctrine. This procedure raised in-
soluble questions as to how an omnipotent, omniscient,
and benevolent God could permit suffering and evil in
nature. A more promising approach, Mathews thought,
would be the empirical approach of Science, spelled with
a capital *S*.

> In the case of any belief, one must begin with a major
> premise furnished either by authority or by induction.
> If one chooses the former, all scientific investigation is
> at an end. If one chooses the latter in religion, a new
> method has been introduced and the organized inherit-
> ance of dogma, rituals and organization is subject to
> investigation and inevitable revaluation.[7]

When religious phenomena were studied widely and em-
pirically, Mathews continued, it became apparent that
the essence of religion was the impulse and effort of
human beings, both individually and socially, to come to
grips with their environment and especially to identify
and establish contact with a superhuman personal element
in that environment. Although science could not prove
the existence of such an element in the environment, it
could lend some warrant to the religious view of the universe and thus help to justify the religious impulse. Scientists, said Mathews, always assumed the intelligibility
of nature. They assumed a correspondence between the
logical structures elaborated by the human mind and the
structures of nature. But if nature was intelligible, it must
be directed or informed by intelligence. That this intelligence had direction and purpose was shown by the course
of organic evolution with its marked tendency toward
higher and more complex forms of interaction between
organism and organism, organism and environment. The

emergence of human personality in the latest stage of this process was the strongest argument of all for the existence of a personal element in nature as a whole. What emerged at the end must have been there from the beginning.

Thus, for Mathews, evolution itself was the chief evidence for the existence and activity of an immanent purpose in the universe. The Bible was reduced to the status of an important historical document attesting the upward progress of the religious impulse. It did so more strikingly, yet in the same general way, that other religious phenomena testified to the same effect. Science, not Scripture, justified a religious view of nature, for science alone revealed nature's aim toward the development of personality. Thereby science contributed "not only a method of testing the legitimacy and value of religion, but also . . . thought patterns with which one may set forth its nature." To do the will of God, for example, was to "grow less animal, less mechanistic, more personal, more regardful of others' personality, more possessed of good will," just as the evolutionary process had. Sin was a stubborn clinging to outmoded values, a refusal to leave one's animal past behind and move onward and upward toward higher personal values in accordance with the immanent law of progress. Salvation meant adjusting oneself to this immanent purpose, "with consequent progress and happiness."

> This struggle against the impersonal forces of nature towards larger social control in the interests of freedom and self-direction must be carried on, since it is in response to the immanent Will. . . . It is a creative experiment carried on in cooperation with the God of that which is ever becoming. . . . Its goal is not an explanation of the universe, but a life with that reason and purpose and personality which science increasingly warrants it in assuming in the universe. . . . we are a part of all that we see, fellow-workers in the process which is carrying life away from its biological and chemical inheritances toward the half-glimpsed, but ever-approached freedom of the completed personality.[8]

Written in the heyday of Protestant modernism, Mathews' plea affords a striking example of science-oriented natural theology postulating evolution as the central fact of existence. Mathews says little or nothing concerning *the* creation as an event in the past. He stresses instead the creative activity of an immanent purpose, a purpose operating according to law and achieving its ends by natural means. The idea of God's transcendence slips into the background or disappears entirely. One senses an implicit dualism in this world view, as if God were struggling to achieve a victory over the impersonal forces of nature. He is immanent in nature but not in complete command of it. At times He seems to become identified with life process, or vital activity, conceived as locked in mortal struggle with inorganic nature. This is scarcely the traditional Christian God. From Mathews' position it is only a step or two to the evolutionary naturalism of Julian Huxley.

Whether Christian or not, Mathews' view was certainly not a biblical view. Its leading ideas were derived from biology and comparative religion, not from Scripture. The Bible was simply a part of the comparative source material upon which conclusions concerning the evolution of religion were based. The Christian faith was recommended, not with the claim that it sprang from a unique divine self-disclosure, but rather on the ground that its doctrine, when pruned of certain historical excrescences, was better adapted than that of any other religion then known to promote the onward advance of man and society in accordance with the immanent will to progress.

The comfortable belief in progress implicit in modernist versions of Christianity was shaken to its foundations by the events of the twentieth century—two devastating world wars, a great economic depression, and the nightmare of totalitarian dictatorship. These events, rather than any development in natural science, produced the violent reaction in Protestant theology known as neo-orthodoxy.

Only those who are old enough to remember the particular kind of desiccated humanism, almost empty of other-worldly content, which prevailed in many Protestant areas in the early decades of this century [writes Douglas Horton] can understand the surprise, the joy, the refreshment which could have been brought by [Karl Barth's book *The Word of God and the Word of Man*] to the ordinary, and, like myself, somewhat desultory reader of the religious literature of that time. To question evolutionary modes of thought in that day was something like questioning the Ptolemaic theory in the time of Copernicus. . . . The very suggestion that this was unsound thinking—the sight of it beginning to totter under Barth's pressure—was to be filled with misgivings, to anticipate crisis. On the other hand, there was undeniable exhilaration rehearing and relearning that God is God, that he *will* will what he will *will,* that he is not caught in the trammels of the world he himself has created, and that man can produce him neither as the conclusion of a syllogism, the Q.E.D. of an experiment, or the crown of a civilization. To encounter the unsettling quality of this frighteningly new and securely old thinking was to enter into a situation Barth called "existential"—a word to whose modern currency Barth himself was one of the first to contribute.[9]

The questioning of evolutionary modes of thought to which Horton alludes was not a questioning of the theory of organic evolution. It was rather a questioning whether the concepts of evolutionary biology were adequate or appropriate to express the Christian view of reality. It was a questioning whether Christian liberalism, in its enthusiasm for evolutionary modes of thought, had not surrendered the central biblical insights concerning nature, man, and God. The doctrine of original sin, for example, was given new meaning by the horrors of the concentration camp and the awful carnage of world war. Confidence in human reason was staggered by a view of the uses to which intelligence could be put. Theology came back to life. The Scriptures spoke to men with renewed power. Once more the word of God was exalted above the word of man.

But although neo-orthodoxy returned to fundamental Christian doctrines, it was not fundamentalist in the usual sense of that word. It exalted the Bible, but not as a textbook of science. Its central position was, and is, that there are important dimensions of reality that are inaccessible to science and cannot be expressed adequately in the forms of logical discourse. These dimensions include the existential relationships of human persons to each other and to God (the so-called I-Thou relationships), the value aspect of reality, and man's consciousness of freedom and moral responsibility. These aspects of experience are of peculiar concern to religion, since religion seeks to comprehend man's existential situation as a free and responsible agent.

To this problem, say the neo-orthodox, science can give no answer because science excludes the problem a priori. The scientist does not raise the problem of his own existence or of existence in general, nor is he, as scientist, concerned with values. He takes the value of scientific activity for granted. He takes existence for granted and seeks to subsume phenomena under certain abstract categories, excluding value categories. He is concerned not with freedom but with determination, with functional relationships among phenomena. Consequently, science cannot discover the meaning and value of human existence, nor can it grasp life's inner unity. As Reinhold Niebuhr puts it:

> Neither the vital thrust of life, nor its organic unities, nor its disharmonies, nor its highest possibilities can be expressed in terms of logic and rational consistency. The dynamic and creative energy of life can be described but not comprehended by reason. The unities of life are organic, and reason can only logically assemble after analytically dividing, thus reducing the organic to a mechanical unity. The disharmonies of life are paradoxically related to its harmonies, as mechanism is paradoxically related to the world of meaning and purpose, and every rational scheme of coherence fails to do

justice to the tragic realities of evil and to its paradoxical relation with the good.[10]

In Niebuhr's opinion, philosophy is as impotent as science to penetrate to ultimate reality.

But if science and philosophy can give no answer to the ultimate questions of existence, how are they to be answered? In the view of Karl Barth, one of the founders of neo-orthodoxy, our knowledge of God and of the meaning of human existence is derived from the Bible and from the events recorded therein. We look to the Bible, says Barth, "not so much to give us knowledge about this particular or that, as to indicate to us the beginning and the end, the origin and the limit, the creative unity and the last problem of all knowledge."

> "In the beginning God created the heavens and the earth" and "Amen. Even so, come, Lord Jesus." Such is the meaning of the world according to the Bible. It is our part to confirm it in our own lives by laboring to relate ourselves, our daily task, and our hour of history to God the Creator and Redeemer. It is not a meaning apart from other meanings, for in it all others—the meanings of natural science, of history, of esthetics, and of religion—are at once included and concluded; and this meaning in the last analysis will be found to be identical with that of philosophy, so far as philosophy understands itself. It is the meaning *par excellence*, without rivals, without challengers, the meaning *sub specie aeterni*. What more can we desire? [11]

But how does the Bible give us knowledge of God? Not by any kind of rational demonstration, not by promulgating a body of doctrine about Him, not by describing stages in man's gradually improving conception of God, but rather by recounting a series of events and human reactions to them which are intelligible only when viewed as the participants in those events viewed them, namely, as acts in which a personal God disclosed His will and purpose for mankind. The events make sense only on the assumption that God was their cause and

disposer. The decisive characteristic of the Bible, says
Barth, is its "striking continuity of faithfulness, constancy,
patient hopefulness, and objective attention toward the
incomprehensible, unpsychological, and unhistorical truth
of God." Through historical narrative, poetry, proverbs,
and saga or myth the Bible points steadfastly to the
ultimate reality underlying not only the biblical history,
not only human history in the large, but the whole of creation.

Consistently with this view of the Bible, Barth inter-
prets the creation stories in Genesis as sagas expressive
of Israel's complete dependence on Yahweh, the God of
Abraham, Isaac, and Jacob. Creation is not so much an
event as a relationship between God and the world, and,
more especially, Israel's world.

> The Bible speaks in Genesis 1 and 2 of events which lie
> outside our historical knowledge [writes Barth]. But it
> speaks upon the basis of knowledge, which is related
> to history. In fact, the wonderful thing about the biblical
> creation narratives is that they stand in strict connexion
> with the history of Israel and so with the story of God's
> action in the covenant with man.[12]

For Christians, says Barth, the knowledge of God the
Creator derives, not from the study of nature, but
from faith that God Himself took on the form of a
creature in Jesus Christ.

> Knowledge of creation is knowledge of God and conse-
> quently *knowledge of faith* in the deepest and ultimate
> sense. It is not just a vestibule in which natural theology
> might find a place. How should we recognise this pa-
> ternity of God, were it not manifest to us in the Son?
> So it is not the existence of the world in its manifold-
> ness, from which we are to read off the fact that God is
> its Creator. The world with its sorrow and its happiness
> will always be a dark mirror to us, about which we may
> have optimistic or pessimistic thoughts; but it gives us
> no information about God as the Creator. But always,
> when man has tried to read the truth from sun, moon

and stars or from himself, the result has been an idol. But when God has been known and then known again in the world, so that the result was a joyful praise of God in creation, that is because He is to be sought and found by us in Jesus Christ. By becoming man in Jesus Christ, the fact has also become plain and credible that God is the Creator of the world. We have no alternative source of revelation.[13]

With these words Barth takes his leave of natural theology—of William Paley, John Ray, and the whole tradition they represented. In so doing, he returns to the sixteenth century Reformers and their distinction between regenerate and unregenerate reason. If there is any revelation of God in His creation, Barth argues, it is apparent only to the eye of faith, only to reason sanctified by trust in the saving Event witnessed by Scripture. As for science, it is free to go its way unmolested. It has nothing to say about God or about creation.

The Christian Confession has in course of the centuries passed through more than one world-picture. And its representatives were always ill-advised when they believed that this or that world-picture was an adequate expression for what the Church, apart from creation, has to think. Christian faith is fundamentally free in regard to all world-pictures, that is, to all attempts to regard what exists by the measure and with the means of the dominant science of the time.[14]

Barth's total rejection of natural theology represents the extreme limit of the reaction against evolutionary modernism in the Protestant camp. Not all neo-orthodox theologians would go so far. Emil Brunner, for example, agrees with Barth that sin obscures man's perception of God's glory in nature, but he insists that the glory is there. God is necessarily revealed in His works, however blind sinful man may be to this revelation.

What the natural man knows of God, of the law and of his own dependence on God, may be very confused and

distorted [writes Brunner]. But even so it is the necessary, indispensable point of contact for divine grace.
This is also proved by the fact that, on the whole, the
New Testament did not create new words, but uses those
that were created by the religious consciousness of the
pagans.[15]

In Brunner's view, natural theology is still possible, but
not natural theology of a demonstrative kind.

The wrong way of making contact [with unbelievers] is
. . . to prove the existence of God. For this presupposes
the Roman Catholic view of *theologia naturalis,* a self-
sufficient rational system of natural knowledge of God.
But though proof is excluded, this does not exclude the
possibility of a discussion pointing towards such evidence
of the existence of God as we have.[16]

Reinhold Niebuhr, too, accepts Barth's view that science and philosophy cannot deal adequately with the
aspects of reality that are of chief concern to religion.
These aspects, says Niebuhr, find their proper expression in myth—not myth as fairy tale but as symbolic expression of an objective reality. But Niebuhr objects to
making acceptance of the Christian myth an act of sheer
faith. Some myths, he says, express our deepest intuitions more adequately than others.

Great myths have actually been born out of profound
experience and are constantly subject to verification by
experience. . . . The ideal of love is not a caprice of
mythology. It is not true because the Cross has revealed
it. The Cross justifies itself to human faith because it
symbolizes an ideal which establishes points of rele-
vance with the deepest experiences and insights of
human life.[17]

Thus, whereas Barth makes Christian faith prerequi-
site for the discovery of God in nature, Niebuhr finds
some verification of Christian myth in the intimations of
ultimate reality that human experience provides. This is
natural theology of a sort, but not of the demonstrative

kind familiar in Christian history. The experience Niebuhr relies on does not concern nature "out there," viewed in scientific detachment and abstraction. It concerns nature concretely apprehended by the whole man—nature-lover, poet, craftsman, naturalist. Above all, it concerns nature as experienced in man's own being. Nature thus experienced reveals, not unambiguous evidences of wise design, but "dynamic and organic qualities in reality which cannot be stated in rational terms." It discloses "paradoxical qualities which elude the canons of logic." Apart from revelation these intimations of reality are confused and contradictory, but in the myth of creation, which represents God as both immanent and transcendent, they find consummate expression and ultimate resolution.

In the writings of Helmut Richard Niebuhr and Paul Tillich, natural religion based on philosophical inquiry and religious experience receives a degree of recognition as providing the "raw material" that revelation transforms and reworks. Revelation, says H. R. Niebuhr, is "the fulfillment and the radical reconstruction of our natural knowledge about the deity through the revelation of one whom Jesus Christ called 'Father.'"

> Revelation imparts no new beliefs about natural or historical facts; it does involve the radical reconstruction of all our beliefs, since these always reflect both human provincialism and concern for self with its idols as well as objective knowledge. The story of the creation in six days is not a part of revelation; yet the account in Genesis, with its dominant interest in God and its partial displacement of man from the central place in the drama of becoming, represents at least the partial reconstruction of ancient beliefs in consequence of revelation. The reconstruction was not complete, for the revolution faith brings to belief is also permanent.[18]

Paul Tillich agrees with Emil Brunner that revelation would have no vehicle without a previous religious experience in terms of which it could be expressed. Defining revelation as "the divine criticism and transformation of religious experience," Tillich finds an element of revelation in all religious experience, in the religious experience of Parmenides, Plato, and Spinoza as well as that of Paul or Isaiah.

> Every doctrine of God is theology of historical revelation in so far as it is rooted in a revelation received in history. Every doctrine of God presupposes faith; for faith is correlated to revelation. Natural theology without preceding faith is nonsense, while natural theology which has the foundation in faith and revelation is not natural theology at all but theology of historical revelation, the only theology which is possible.[19]

Thus, Tillich erases the distinction between revealed and natural theology by extending the scope of revelation. For the traditional dichotomy of natural and revealed theology he substitutes a single theology with two poles: the question posed by man's reflection on his own existence, and the answer provided by divine revelation.

In the Roman Catholic Church and in some branches of Protestantism, notably the Anglican branch, there has been no such general retreat from natural theology as has taken place among the neo-orthodox. Catholic theologians have been quick to point out that only the last of St. Thomas' five proofs of the existence of God was directly affected by Darwin's theory. With respect to the fifth proof, they argue that it was William Paley's watchmaker analogy rather than St. Thomas' argument from the uniform modes of behavior of natural agents that was drawn into question by the theory of natural selection. Paley's analogy of mechanical contrivance suggested a creation finished once and for all at some moment or period in time. St. Thomas, on the other hand, argued from the fact that natural agents act in determinate and uniform ways according to their specific natures, adding that all these agents work together harmoniously, as if ordered to a general end. This order and uniformity in the actions of individual agents and of all natural agents collectively was unintelligible, said Aquinas, unless one acknowledged a Supreme Intelligence directing things to their proper ends.

St. Thomas' fifth way was thus more adaptable to an evolutionary science than the physicotheology of John Ray and William Paley. It asserted that the internal harmony and external adaptation of living organisms presupposed an intelligent ordering of the actions producing them, but it did not necessarily imply that God created the progenitors of each species of plant and animal at some instant of time, endowing them with exactly the organs and instincts required for the continuation of the species. To the argument of Darwin and Huxley that random variation and natural selection sufficed to explain the adaptations of structure to function in the organic world the natural theologian could reply that, although processes of variation might modify organisms and environmental circumstances might favor the spread of some varieties at the expense of others, nevertheless the organisms themselves must already be present as going concerns. Variation does not create, but only modifies, the internal harmony of the organism and its adaptation to the environment; these require an adequate explanation. If the argument is pushed back to the origin of organized beings and the question is raised whether chance combinations of atoms or molecules could produce living beings capable of reproducing themselves, this question is still not decisive. Assuming that they could, one may still ask whence the organization evident in molecules and atoms and whence the uniformity and order apparent in their behavior. As Father Maurice R. Holloway puts it, returning to the basic argument of St. Thomas' fifth way:

. . . in the very first combination of the simplest elements or gases, or whatever we call the primordial material being, there was activity. And being existential activity, it was a determined kind of activity. Why did this first particle act this way rather than that? Why did it act at all? If it acted at all, it acted in a determined way, and if it acted in a determined way, it was ordered to this act. And if it was ordered in this act, this order was intended. . . . Now a scientist, as a scientist, may not be expected to follow this reasoning, since it is philosophical rather than scientific; but it is not for that reason any less real or legitimate. The scientist as a philosopher, or maybe even as man, should be able to see it, provided he is willing to exercise his intelligence outside the limits of a strictly positive scientific method.[20]

As this passage shows, Catholic writers distinguish between questions and methods of inquiry appropriate to natural science and those appropriate to philosophy. Science, says the distinguished Catholic philosopher Étienne Gilson, is concerned with describing *what* natural things are and *how* they interact; it does not investigate the *why,* the cause or causes, of their existence. Why is there anything at all? And why do the things that exist act in regular and uniform ways? These questions, says Gilson, are metaphysical questions demanding metaphysical answers. For their solution they require the whole Aristotelian apparatus of material, efficient, formal, and final causes. To wave them aside as "unscientific," as if science exhausted the field of rational inquiry, is to restrict arbitrarily the scope of reason.

To ask the question why, out of an infinity of possible combinations of physico-chemical elements, there has arisen the living and thinking being we call man is to seek the cause why such a complex of physical energies as man actually is, or exists. In other words, it is to inquire into the possible causes for the *existence* of living and thinking organisms upon earth. The hypothesis that living substances may tomorrow be produced by biochemists in their laboratories is irrelevant to the question. If a chemist ever succeeds in turning out cells, or some elementary sorts of organisms, nothing will be easier for him than to say why such organisms exist. His answer will be: I made them. Our own question is not at all: Are living and thinking beings made up of nothing else than physical elements? It rather is: Supposing they ultimately consist of nothing else, how can we account for the *existence* of the very order of molecules which produces what we call life, and thought?

Scientifically speaking, such problems do not make sense. . . . When asked why there are such organized beings, scientists answer: Chance. Now anybody may fluke a brilliant stroke at billiards; but when a billiard player makes a run of a hundred, to say that he fluked it is to offer a rather weak explanation. Some scientists know this so well that they substitute for the notion of chance the notion of mechanical laws, which is its very reverse. But when they come to explaining how these mechanical laws have given rise to living organized beings, they are driven back to chance as to the last reason it is possible to quote. . . . Why should those eminently rational beings, the scientists, deliberately prefer to the simple notions of design, or purposiveness, in nature, the arbitrary notions of blind force, chance, emergence, sudden variation, and similar ones? Simply because they much prefer a complete absence of intelligibility to the presence of a nonscientific intelligibility.[21]

The distinction between the scientific and the philosophic approach to nature is very common in Catholic writing concerning evolution, but there are signs that some writers regard this distinction, however valid and necessary, as an inadequate answer to the challenge of Darwinism and neo-Darwinism. In a recent article in *The New Scholasticism*, Father Raymond J. Nogar takes Catholic philosophers to task for relying on it too heavily:

In the name of professional respect [says Father Nogar], the philosopher gives the biologist a free hand, having no interest or concern for his theories until they patently and publicly conflict with some metaphysical principle. But when such assertions are made publicly, the ready reply is that the scientist is speaking out of his field, as a philosopher, and (benignly) not a good one. What the philosopher apparently fails to understand is that when the Darwinist asserts openly that chance is the sufficient reason for the organization of the world, and denies outright the existence of intrinsic finality among organisms, or [asserts] that organic agents simply do not act for any purpose or end, he is calmly saying what is intrinsic to his biological theory of the evolution of species. This is not an unwarranted extrapolation, an inferential extension, of Darwinian theory; it is inherent in the very theory itself, and has been all along.[22]

If the significance of evolutionary biology for philosophy and theology is to be determined, Father Nogar continues, there must be co-operation between the biologist and the philosopher of nature, not mutual isolation and false respect. By way of illustration, Father Nogar examines the methodological problems involved in answering the question how far the *fact* of evolution may be said to have been scientifically demonstrated. He first points out that Darwin himself, although he believed that scientific evidence warranted the conclusion that animals were descended from four or five prototypes, regarded the hypothesis that *all* animals and plants were descended from a single prototype as an inference grounded chiefly on analogy. Father Nogar then examines the opinions of two modern paleontologists, George Gaylord Simpson and O. H. Schindewolf, concerning the extent to which the fossil record corroborates the theory of monophyletic evolution. He concludes that biologists today are no closer to being able to prove the descent of all living forms from a single prototype than Darwin was.

Father Nogar's main purpose, however, is not to show that monophyletic evolution has not been scientifically established. It is rather to urge the necessity of close co-operation between biologists and scientifically-informed philosophers in establishing canons of biological methodology as a first step in clarifying the philosophical and theological issues raised by evolutionary biology.

> The great disservice which modern thinkers have done to the cause of scientific biology and natural philosophy by driving a wedge between these two approaches to the organic world is markedly apparent in the important question of the evolution of species. Aristotle was much more wise and realistic when he founded and elaborated a systematic treatment of the world of living organisms in which the natural philosopher and the theoretical biologist were one in theory and in fact. Today, in the name of formal professional exclusiveness, these two

disciplines are estranged, completely inadequate and incompetent without each other. If, because of the wealth of details of organic data available to us today, it is practicable to have some division of labor, the two must of necessity be rewedded in professional co-operation. *For until the natural philosopher and the theoretical biologist, in a co-operative and professional effort, elaborate canons of biological methodology, and apply those canons to the best available data on organic process, the question of the fact and the theory of organic evolution will remain an unverifiable and unintelligible matter to both.*[23]

Before leaving the subject of Catholic philosophy and evolutionary biology, let us see what a Thomistic interpretation of evolution looks like. An example is provided in J. R. E. Ramirez's article "The Ultimate Why of Evolution," published in the Darwin centennial issue of *The New Scholasticism*. In this article Ramirez defines evolution as "the specific process which, entailing a multiplicity of changes, constitutes the motion from one type of living material form to another type." His question then is: "Supposing final causality and supposing that evolution is operative or has taken place, does this process have a specific end or only as many ends as there are products of it; and if it does have a specific end, what is it?" In answering this question he first undertakes to show that the evolutionary process cannot be identified with the material beings entering into it or emerging from it, nor with change in general, nor with diversity of form as such, nor with the hierarchy observable among living organisms, nor with the known order of secondary causes.

Evolution necessarily implies all these things but cannot be identified with them. . . . Once we concede that matter as such need not necessarily imply evolution, we can see that neither does change, nor secondary causality; for these could still truly exist even if we had only local motion. As for a hierarchy of living beings, this could certainly be the result of direct creation. . . . Finally, diversity implies evolution least of all.[24]

Since these things—matter, change, diversity, hierarchy, secondary causality—are more ultimate than evolution, evolution cannot be *their* final cause. But can these things give the why of evolution? Examining this question, Ramirez concludes that although evolution cannot be said to exist for the sake of matter or for the sake of hierarchy or of change per se, it may be said to exist both for the sake of a special community of matter in diversity and for the sake of a special type of secondary causality.

> The ultimate why of evolution is to have oneness, continuity, ancestry, a continuum of similitude in changing things ordered to diversity. Evolution insures this continuum directly, through matter, space and time, and it insures nothing else. In a sense this continuum of material community may even be said to be what evolution *is,* what it signifies most profoundly; but it is also its why, its end. Evolution exists directly for the sake of the continuum itself, that in whatever intended change or whatever intended diversity, material things might preserve a certain kinship or similarity through a continuity as it were of ancestry or origin—an origin possibly traceable to a unique material form and to a unique act of origination. More simply, evolution exists that all material things might comprise one family in the deepest meaning of the term. . . .
>
> Together with the fundamental purpose of material community, evolution has another end or purpose linked with but distinct from the first: secondary causality. Evolution exists that secondary causes related to each other or materially derived from each other might exist and exercise their own proportionate efficient causality.[25]

If these are the final causes of evolution, Ramirez continues, many traditional objections against the idea of purposiveness in evolution are without foundation. The randomness and planlessness frequently said to characterize evolution, its failure to move consistently in the direction of higher forms of organization, the failure of some organisms to develop fully, the evil inherent in the cycle of life and death—none of these constitutes a convincing argument against purposiveness in evolution if the purpose of evolution is not to "go somewhere" or to maximize pleasure and minimize pain but rather to achieve "the continuum of secondary causes and of material ancestry or community in changing things ordered to diversity." "This very special community of matter," Ramirez concludes, "will never cease to be realized so long as evolution continues."

As we have seen, Catholic thought distinguishes between scientific theories and the philosophical views associated with them. The latter are then considered on their philosophical merits. In such a critique Catholic philosophy draws heavily, though not exclusively, on Aristotle. But Aristotle's is by no means the only philosophy capable of providing a critique of the mechanistic cosmology and nominalistic view of reality assumed by Darwin and other nineteenth century evolutionists. As a matter of fact, evolutionary biology itself contained the seeds of a philosophical revolution. Taken in conjunction with exciting new developments in physics, it rendered the Newtonian world machine as obsolete as Paley's watchmaker analogy. It gave rise to new ways of looking at the universe. To Henri Bergson and William James it suggested that the universe was a dynamic flux that eluded the abstractions of science and philosophy. For Charles Peirce it constituted a decisive refutation of nominalism and of the prevailing conception of the laws of nature as fixed and unchanging. To Alfred North Whitehead it suggested the idea that organism rather than mechanism was the key concept in the philosophy of nature.

These innovations in philosophy have had more influence in Protestant than in Roman Catholic circles. Whitehead, in particular, has made a deep impression on Protestant thought. A comparison of Bishop Frederick Temple's views on evolution and religion in 1884 with those of his illustrious son, Archbishop William Temple, a half century later will serve to suggest the extent of Whitehead's influence on Anglican theology.

In Frederick Temple's lectures, published two years after Darwin's death, we find ourselves in the mechanistic world of the nineteenth century. For Bishop Temple, as for Darwin, the theory of evolution was simply an extension to the organic world of the Newtonian concept of nature as a law-bound system of matter in motion. Just as Laplace had explained the origin of the solar system by the nebular hypothesis, so Darwin had explained the origin of species by discerning the natural processes governing their extinction and modification. But this explanation, said Bishop Temple, did not destroy the traditional arguments for the existence of God. A special act of creation may not have been necessary to give each species of plant and animal existence, but when evolution was traced back to its beginnings, however remote, there must still have been an original act of creation—"creation not of matter only, but of the various kinds of matter, and of the laws governing all and each of those kinds, and of the distribution of this matter in space."

As for Paley's argument from design, it too was substantially unaffected by the theory of evolution, Bishop Temple declared. What was discredited was Paley's conception of the manner in which the Creator had acted to bring about the adaptations evident in nature. Instead of an instantaneous act, there had been a long, slow development, an unfolding of potentialities implanted in the original elements of matter. Such an evolving creation, exhibiting perpetual progress toward higher forms of life and higher modes of adaptation, afforded even more striking testimony to the wisdom of the Creator than the finished creation assumed by Paley. Whereas Paley's argument left open the possibility that several designers had been at work, evolution required a single designer of the whole process. In short, the argument from design had been strengthened, not weakened, by Darwin's work.

There is still as much as ever the proof of intelligent purpose pervading all creation. The difference is that the execution of that purpose belongs more to the original act of creation, less to acts of government since. There is more divine foresight, there is less divine interposition; and whatever has been taken from the latter has been added to the former.[26]

Despite his vigorous defense of Paley, Bishop Temple could no longer regard the argument from design as the main pillar of natural theology. Nor did he place much confidence in the traditional five ways of St. Thomas Aquinas. Instead, following the lead of Immanuel Kant and Bishop Joseph Butler, he rested the argument primarily on the moral imperative felt in every human breast.

> The voice within us which demands our acceptance of religion makes no direct appeal to the evidence supplied by the senses. We are called on to believe in a supreme law of duty on pain of being lowered before our own consciences. And this law of duty goes on to assert its own supremacy over all things that exist, and that not as an accidental fact, but as inherent in its essence. And this supremacy cannot be other than an accidental fact unless it be not only actual but intended. And intention implies personality; and the law thus shows itself to be a Supreme Being, claiming our reverence, and asserting Himself to be the Creator, the R… and the Judge of all things that are. . . . W… are to believe not because the truth of this voice … proved independently of itself, but simply … …use we are commanded. Corrob… …ve evidence may be looked for else-…here, but the main, the primary evidence is within the soul.[27]

In this argument, Bishop Temple yielded much of the ground occupied by traditional natural theology in favor of a position prepared by one of the severest critics of that theology, Immanuel Kant. But his retreat was not complete. He still used some of the traditional arguments, including Paley's physicotheology, but he regarded them as corroborative rather than demonstrative. The fundamental proof of God's existence was the still, small voice of conscience.

Turning from the writings of Bishop Frederick Temple to those of his son William fifty years later, we enter a new world philosophically speaking, a world in which A. N. Whitehead is the presiding philosophical genius. In this world of ideas organism is the basic concept. Nature is no longer viewed as a self-contained system of matter in motion operating independently of the minds that observe it. Instead, it is a process of becoming, a process in which everything—the atom and the electron as well as the star, the crystal, and the sea urchin—becomes what it is by interaction with everything else that is. In this universal process the mental activity of conscious human organisms is of unique importance. Through their capacity to form "free ideas," these organisms are able to grasp the nature and discern the historical development of the process itself. In so doing, they transcend the process.

> Some men [writes Archbishop Temple] have . . . been so overwhelmed by the greatness of the known world as to deny all significance to the knowing mind. *But this fact of knowledge is more remarkable than all the varieties of known objects put together. For the mind which knows is in a perfectly real sense equal to what it knows, and in another real sense transcends it, unless what it knows is another mind which also knows. . . . That there should "emerge" in the cosmic process a capacity to apprehend, even in a measure to comprehend, that process is the most remarkable characteristic of the process itself. . . . Thus the cosmic process gives evidence that it is not only process, and history supplies the proof that reality is more than historical.*[28]

But how is the emergence of knowing organisms within the universal process to be accounted for? Only on the assumption that the process is grounded in a Supreme Mind which knows and thus transcends it, Archbishop Temple answers. Whatever emerges in the world process must have an adequate ground in that process. If one begins with the motions of valueless, mindless matter or the transformations of mindless, valueless energy, he will have difficulty in arriving at intelligent, morally responsible persons. But if, on the contrary, he begins with the knowing, purposive activity of He Who Is, the facts of experience become intelligible. The scientist's search for truth becomes intelligible. Man's discovery of beauty and goodness in the world becomes intelligible. The great fact of human love and fellowship becomes intelligible.

> Personality exhibits itself supremely in purposes of fellowship or love—supremely, because here is it furthest removed from the mechanical or organic. Therefore it needs, for its full self-expression the existence of other persons. If we take as our ultimate principle Personality, not only as purposive mind, but as mind of which the actual purpose is love, then the occurrence of persons within the World-Process is truly explained by the principle to which that process is referred; and there is no other principle known to us whereby human fellowship, which is the culmination of the Process hitherto, is truly explained at all.[29]

To assert the personality of the Ground of Existence is to assert the doctrine of creation, Archbishop Temple continues.

> . . . if we begin with the world and find that it points us to a personal ground of its existence, the relation of the world to such ground of its being must be that of creature to Creator. For the essence of the doctrine of Creation is not that God inaugurated the existence of the world at a particular moment of time, but that it owes its existence—not only its beginning—to His volitional activity. The doctrine of Creation denies that the world proceeds from the Divine Being by any process of inevitable emanation; it denies that God and the World are correlates, so that each depends upon the other for existence in the same way; it asserts that the world exists because God chose to call it into being and chooses to sustain it in being. If he is personal, and if He is the ground of the world's existence, this follows as an inevitable consequence . . . "Thou has created all things, and because of thy will they were, and were created." [30]

This argument is as interesting for what it omits as for what it includes. There is, for example, no trace of

Paley's watchmaker analogy, nor is there any appeal to "progress" as proof of the divine superintendence of nature and history. The point of view is evolutionary, but in a very broad, Whiteheadian sense. Process, rather than evolution, is the central concept. The arguments are strictly metaphysical, seeking an adequate cause for the existence of knowing, valuing, loving persons. In this respect they represent a return to something like Thomistic natural theology, though in a Whiteheadian, rather than an Aristotelian, context. Finally, they manifest in a high degree the tendency in modern Christian thought to divorce natural theology from reliance on the specific content of natural science. The metaphysical demand for an adequate cause of the existence of human beings is equally relevant whether one adopts an evolutionary or a non-evolutionary point of view in biology. It can be evaded only by denying the legitimacy of the demand.

Generally speaking, modern biologists and paleontologists have shown little enthusiasm for theistic interpretations of evolution of the sort we have described. Like Darwin, most of them have difficulty in discovering evidence of design or purpose in the processes of variation and natural selection. Yet, curiously enough, their vocabulary is frequently replete with words that in ordinary usage imply purpose, striving, aspiration, realization of value. We can illustrate this schizophrenic discrepancy between formal philosophic attitude and everyday biological vocabulary with reference to the writings of Julian Huxley. Huxley is resolutely antitheistic. In his recent book *Evolution in Action,* he declares that there is no evidence of design or purpose in nature apart from man and his purposes. Speaking of the inorganic realm, he says:

> Nowhere in all its vast extent is there any trace of purpose, or even of prospective significance. It is impelled from behind by blind physical forces, a gigantic and chaotic jazz dance of particles and radiations, in which the only over-all tendency we have so far been able to

detect, is summarized in the second law of thermo-dynamics—the tendency to run down.[31]

The world of living things, Huxley goes on, *appears* to exhibit intelligent adaptation of structure to function, but the appearance is illusory. Darwin's theory, confirmed and extended by the science of genetics, shows that the adaptation which prevails is an outcome of random variation, genetic recombination, and natural selection. Natural selection, declares Huxley:

> . . . converts randomness into direction, and blind chance into apparent purpose. It operates with the aid of time to produce improvements in the machinery of living, and in the process generates results of more than astronomical improbability, which could have been achieved in no other way. But it has its limitations. It is opportunist, and it is relative: at any one time it can only produce results which are of immediate biological advantage to their possessors, in relation to the particular situation of the moment. So it can never plan ahead or work to a complete design. Furthermore, it often leads life into blind alleys, from which there is no evolutionary escape.[32]

In this passage we encounter at once the metaphorical vocabulary of much modern evolutionary biology. We are presented with the picture of a process, natural selection, which is blind yet opportunistic. It has no directing purpose, yet it can lead life into blind alleys. It aims at no realization of value, yet it produces improvements in the machinery of living. If we ask what the term *improvement* could mean in a planless universe, we are told that it means "improvement of the various pieces of biological machinery by means of which living substance carries on the business of existence and survival." Alternatively, biological improvement is defined as the realization of possibilities. "Living substance," says Huxley, "demonstrates its improvement during evolution by doing old things in new and better ways, by acquiring new properties, by organizing itself in new forms, by increasing its efficiency and enlarging its variety." Now, it appears, "living substance" has become personified and seems to be engaged in purposive activity. This personification turns out to be Huxley's basic metaphor. Huxley defines *improvement, advance, progress, higher, lower,* in terms of life's progressive realization of its inherent potentialities. Improvement in a given group of animals takes place by a deployment, or divergent radiation, that enables the group to extend over more territory, to convert "more and more different kinds of materials into its own living substance" and to do so "more efficiently." Progress, then, is "the way which leads to ever-fresh realizations of new possibilities for living substance." It gives life increased efficiency in dealing with the "challenge" of the environment. It leads life "into regions of new evolutionary opportunity."

> Each new deployment, after steadily advancing over its new terrain, comes to an impasse. There is sometimes a path out of the impasse, but it is generally a devious one; it is through its twists and turns that life finds its way into a new field of maneuver; and this marks the beginning of another distinct step in progress.[33]

The last and most surprising turn in the devious path of progress, Huxley tells us, was the appearance of man. Living substance had by this time, the late Cenozoic period, exhausted all the possibilities of progress but one.

> Only one feature remained capable of improvement— the brain organization and behavior. Only a greater flexibility of behavior, and a higher organization of awareness, enabled living substance to become capable of conceptual thought and symbolic language; and these . . . are the two distinguishing marks of man, and the basis of the latest deployment of life.[34]

With the appearance of man, purely biological progress came to an end. Life had "transcended itself," and evolution became converted "from a mechanical toward a conscious process." The path of biological evolution was closed off, but in its place cultural evolution opened up vast new fields in which living substance could realize new possibilities. And man, in becoming conscious of the whole evolutionary process, came gradually to know his own duty and destiny—"to be the agent of the world process of evolution, the sole agent capable of leading it to new heights, and enabling it to realize new possibilities." [35] Thus man, a free, intelligent, purposive agent, has a responsibility to co-operate with and lead on to new heights a world process of evolution which, apart from man, has no awareness of its own possibilities, no aim to realize them, no intelligence to direct itself—a process for which the pronoun *it* suffices.

If this vocabulary of life's achievements, dead ends, blind alleys, self-transcendence, trials and errors, exploitations of the environment, and forward motion were confined to Huxley's writings, it would not be of great significance. But it is very general, even among those who object to Huxley's attempt to introduce words like *progress* and *improvement* into the language of biology. How are we to explain the persistence of such a vocabulary, plainly at odds with the philosophical beliefs of most biologists? Are these metaphors harmless expressions employed to enliven biological treatises that would otherwise be dull for the general reader? In some cases this may be the explanation. But the phenomenon is too widespread, the habit too inveterate, to admit of so simple an explanation. Does it not rather suggest that these scientists sense a creative element or ground in the evolutionary process, however much their philosophical preconceptions may dispose them to deny its reality?

As a matter of fact, R. A. Fisher and Theodosius Dobzhansky, both eminent geneticists, emphasize the creative character of organic evolution. It is creative, says Fisher, in the sense that it has produced new *kinds* of beings and new *levels* of being, and also in the sense that its course is unpredictable and irreversible. The number of possible gene combinations in an experimentally mixed population of a few thousand wild Drosophila flies is so astronomically large in relation to the number of flies involved that one cannot predict what adaptive combination will occur and thus form the basis for future developments in each of the various experimental cages, Dobzhansky tells us.

> Replicate experiments, with the same genetic materials
> and conducted in similar environments, often give sig-
> nificantly divergent results. In some populations the
> changes may be rapid and in others sluggish; in some,
> balanced equilibria may be established and in others,
> one of the chromosomal types may be lost. . . . The
> replicate populations, though originally alike genetically
> and exposed to like environments, follow different evolu-
> tionary paths.[36]

Although chance determines what combinations appear in
a given cage, viability, or adaptation to the environment
of the cage, determines which of these combinations will
survive to provide the basis for future recombinations and
future evolutionary developments. Thus, genuine chance
is involved in evolution, but the determining factor is, as
Fisher puts it, "the mutual reaction of each organism with
the whole ecological situation in which it lives—the creative action of one species on another." [37]

Thus, we come back to creativity. The fundamental
question seems to be, not whether organic evolution is a
creative process, but whether the idea of a natural creative process makes sense without the inclusion in the
process of a creative ground capable of envisaging the
possibilities inherent in it. If such a creative ground is
recognized as indispensable, there is a philosophical basis
for speaking of the "achievements" of the evolutionary
process, of man's responsibility to assist in the realization
of potential harmonies, and so forth. If a creative ground
is denied, there is no rational justification for a vocabulary
of this kind. We can say that natural processes have produced a development that looks like progress from our
human point of view. We can rhapsodize with Thomas
Henry Huxley, Julian Huxley's grandfather, about "Nature's great progression, from the formless to the formed'
—from the inorganic to the organic—from blind force to
conscious intellect and will." [38] But the fact itself, if it
is a fact, must remain unintelligible, a mystery and a
miracle. We can assert that blind force has produced con-

scious intellect and will, but we can never understand how that could happen. Nor can we draw any conclusion from it concerning man's moral responsibility as a free agent. If we attempt to do so, we are simply talking nonsense. Thomas Huxley was wiser than his grandson on this point. His argument against Herbert Spencer's evolutionary ethics in his famous Romanes lecture applies with equal force to Julian Huxley's attempt to draw moral inspiration from the progress of nature.

Why, then, are so many modern biologists reluctant to recognize a creative ground of organic evolution? Partly, one suspects, because they distrust philosophical reasoning. This attitude is deeply ingrained in modern scientists, but there are powerful forces working to overcome it. The increasing urgency of the population problem and of eugenic problems generally has sharpened the sense of moral responsibility among biologists. If they are to discuss these problems intelligently, they must philosophize. Even on the purely scientific level philosophical reflection is urgently needed. The curious vocabulary of evolutionary biology to which we have alluded is a symptom of a deep-seated clash between inherited philosophical presuppositions and the demands of scientific explanation.

Not all biologists and paleontologists ignore the philosophical and theological problems implicit in the subject matter they study. In the writings of Theodosius Dobzhansky, L. C. Birch, and others, attempts have been made to relate evolutionary theory to the Christian doctrine of creation. To accomplish this, the Australian zoologist L. C. Birch finds it necessary to reject the omnipotent Creator of traditional Christian theology in favor of a Whiteheadian deity who achieves by persuasion such order as is possible in the occasions of experience that make up the creative advance of the universe. Creation by evolution is a slow, continuous process involving innumerable trials and many failures, says Birch.

> Whatever be the inner nature of creativity, it assures us that perfection in any sense is not reached overnight or by any direct path. Nature appears rather to be a huge

experiment, and in that experiment, as in all experiments, there is room for accidents to happen. . . . Natural selection is a selection of random mutations (random in relation to the needs imposed by the environment at the time of the mutation); and many of these mutations do not persist for a single generation. But, despite the seeming waste and the indirect pathways to the adaptation of the living organism to its world, there does emerge a coherence and an integration of the organism which is its life. This is the nature of the creative process in the living world. Dobzhansky gave eloquent expression to this idea . . . when he compared the creative process with the production of a work of art. Both involve the risk of ending in failure. . . . [This] modern understanding of the evolutionary process is not at all incompatible with what might be expected to happen if God is a God of persuasion rather than coercion.[39]

Here again we see the influence of Whitehead's philosophy. Although Birch gives his concept of creation a Christian twist by introducing the idea of the "cost of creation" (he discovers the pattern of the Cross "deeply woven into the very fabric of creation"), his view is more Platonic than Christian. It recalls Plato's *demiurgos* fashioning a cosmos out of recalcitrant matter. Creation *ex nihilo,* the Christian explanation of the act of existence, never comes up for discussion.

Among Catholic scientists, the Jesuit paleontologist Father Teilhard de Chardin has made the boldest and most ambitious effort to cast evolutionary theory into a Christian mold. In his book *The Phenomenon of Man,* he views evolution as "an ascent towards consciousness," a "grand orthogenesis of everything living towards a higher degree of immanent spontaneity." Morphologically, he finds this ascent manifested in the increasing complication of the nervous system. Evolution is "a movement of consciousness veiled by morphology." Human evolution, in turn, is but the latest phase of a general development that must culminate in the union of all conscious souls in a transcendent focus that Father Teilhard calls

Omega, "the principle which at one and the same time makes this involution irreversible and moves and collects it." [40]

The Phenomenon of Man presents a double challenge. As the work of a distinguished paleontologist it challenges current perspectives and theories in evolutionary science. As the effort of a devout Jesuit to reconcile Catholicism with a thoroughgoing evolutionism it raises momentous issues for Catholic philosophy and theology. Father Teilhard insists that he writes as a scientist, not as a philosopher, but his conception of science is very broad. He appeals to rational coherence rather than experimental verification as the test of validity of his vision of nature. Such a criterion is more appropriate to philosophy than to science. But his book is not therefore unimportant for science, as the American paleontologist George Gaylord Simpson seems to think. On the contrary, it suggests a new way of looking at old facts, and this kind of reorientation has proved fruitful in science on more than one occasion. On the philosophical level, Father Teilhard provides a rational basis for the metaphorical vocabulary habitually employed by Simpson and Julian Huxley without a shadow of philosophical justification.

Whether Father Teilhard's theory can be reconciled with Catholic doctrine remains to be seen. The fact that Father Teilhard was refused permission to publish his ideas during his lifetime would seem to indicate that reconciliation is impossible, but one must not judge hastily in matters of this kind. The response to *The Phenomenon of Man* in Catholic circles has been extremely varied, ranging all the way from extravagant praise to contemptuous dismissal. In an article entitled "Christianity and Evolution," cited by an eminent Catholic anthropologist as one of the best short pieces ever written on this problem, Monsignor Bruno de Solages, Rector of the Catholic Institute of Toulouse, praises the "magnificent coherence" of Father Teilhard's view of evolution—"not materialistic, but essentially spiritualistic, not pantheistic but theistic, not deterministic but directed by God, not immanent but requiring the transcendental, not anti-Christian, but leading logically to the Christian supernatural."

> . . . within the framework of a Universe no longer cyclical as was the Aristotelian system—a great clock which eternally moves—but the Universe of modern science—which is an evolutionary Universe, a Universe in progress, and one which, unless it be radically absurd, must necessarily go in a certain direction—Father Teilhard de Chardin successively demonstrates the personal immortality of souls, and the existence of a personal God, the motivating force of all this evolution. . . . And we find that the heart of these two demonstrations is really nothing else basically but the Aristotelian and Thomistic principle, *desiderium naturae non potest esse inane.* "The desire of nature cannot exist in vain." Only, in place of applying this principle merely to the desire of a spirit, considered in its individuality, it is now extended to the totality of spirits, which is considered in the evolutionary perspective of the whole of modern science, as an actual term of the Universe.[41]

At the opposite pole of criticism, Father Raymond J. Nogar finds that, despite widespread non-professional enthusiasm for *The Phenomenon of Man,* "professional philosophers call it bad philosophy, professional theologians call it bad theology, professional poets call it bad poetry, professional scientists call it bad (mystical, which is worse) science, and, whatever its rhetorical advantage, professional dialecticians call it impossible dialogue." [42] In view of these controversies among Catholics, a non-Catholic may perhaps be pardoned for suspending judgment concerning the probable effect of Father Teilhard's writings on Catholic philosophy and natural theology.*

We conclude, then, that natural theology, although it has suffered a decline in some quarters since Darwin's time, is not as moribund as some writers have imagined.

---

* More recently, the Sacred Congregation of the Holy Office has issued a warning to the heads of Catholic educational institutions that the works of Teilhard de Chardin "present ambiguities and even grave errors in philosophical and theological matters."

Physicotheology in the form popularized by John Ray and William Paley is probably gone forever. It assumed a static universe in which the forms of the basic structures of nature were permanent and unchanging, designed by God to serve certain functions in the general economy of nature. Such a view could not survive the accumulation of evidence pointing to the mutability of the structures of nature, nor could it withstand the elaboration of the conception of nature as a law-bound system of matter in motion. But the larger question whether human experience affords intimations or proofs of the existence and attributes of a Supreme Being transcending yet immanent in the universe we inhabit is by no means closed. The facts and theories of evolutionary biology have settled nothing here, for they are subject to an astonishing variety of philosophical interpretations, as anyone who reads James Collins' excellent study "Darwin's Impact on Philosophy" or James Street Fulton's "Philosophical Adventures of the Idea of Evolution 1859–1959" will see.[43] Even the question whether an evolutionary view of reality in the manner of modern process philosophies provides the true key to the mystery of the universe is still open. In any case, the key, whatever it may be, is not likely to be found without bringing man into the picture, without examining that curious creature who interrogates nature in the hope of understanding not only the world but himself, his duty, and his destiny. To the subject of man as he appears in the light of the Darwinian revolution we now turn.

3

Darwin and Social Science

THE IDEA OF CREATING A SOCIAL SCIENCE BY APPLYING the methods of natural science to the study of man and society is nearly as old as modern science itself. Adam Smith took Newton's conception of nature as a law-bound system of matter in motion as his model when he represented society as a collection of individuals pursuing their self-interest in an economic order governed by the laws of supply and demand. In like manner, Herbert Spencer and his contemporaries felt the impact of Darwin's theory of natural selection a century later.

Theories of social evolution did not begin with Darwin. The first examples in modern times are to be found in the mid-eighteenth century, about the time that ideas of organic and cosmic evolution began to circulate in Western society. The same decade of the 1750's that produced Pierre Louis de Maupertuis' evolutionary speculations in biology and Immanuel Kant's sketch of a nebular hypothesis in astronomy gave birth to Jean Jacques Rousseau's famous *Essay on the Origin and Foundations of Inequality among Men,* in which Rousseau undertook to trace man's development from a solitary, bestial condition to his present civilized state. Not that Rousseau believed in organic evolution. On the contrary, he insisted that man was the only species capable of progress; man alone could perfect himself by using his intellect to improve his condition. Where, then, did Rousseau get the idea that man had begun his career as an intelligent but relatively defenseless animal? Unquestionably he was influenced by travellers' accounts of orang-outangs, wolf boys, and savage Hottentots. But these were not the only source of his revolutionary anthropology. Rousseau performed an interesting thought experiment. Whereas Thomas Hobbes and John Locke had arrived at their ideas concerning man's natural state by thinking away the institution of government, Rousseau attempted in imagination to strip human nature of all attributes derived from society, including the marvellous attribute of language. He soon discovered that man apart from society was little more than an animal, dependent for survival on the use of his brain. Man's distinguishing faculty was his ability to perfect himself. The verb *perfect* in this context did not mean to achieve some ideal or fulfillment of human nature, whether individually or socially. It meant simply to improve one's lot by taking thought, by collaborating with other men in the same predicament, by learning to control nature (and perhaps also one's fellow man) for one's own benefit. Perfection was an endless process because the intellect could develop indefinitely. Mental development, in turn, created new needs, new passions, new desires. Society arose, bringing in its wake property and the dominance of one man over others by force and fraud. The whole process was morally ambiguous. According to Rousseau, writes Arthur O. Lovejoy in a brilliant essay:

> There is a dual process going on through history: on the one hand, an indefinite progress in all those powers and achievements which express merely the potency of man's intellect; on the other hand, an increasing estrangement of men from one another, an intensification of ill-will and mutual fear, culminating in a monstrous epoch of universal conflict and mutual destruction. And the chief cause of the latter process Rousseau, following Hobbes and Mandeville, found . . . in that unique passion of the self-conscious and social animal—pride, self-

esteem, *le besoin de se mettre au-dessus des autres.*[1]

"A large survey of history does not belie these generalizations," Lovejoy adds, "and the history of the period since Rousseau wrote lends them a melancholy verisimilitude."

In the early nineteenth century Rousseau's misgivings concerning the progress of civilization were largely forgotten, but his idea of tracing the evolution of human nature from brute-like beginnings took hold with a vengeance. Theories of social evolution proliferated like mushrooms. The impetus to their elaboration came less from biology than from a growing awareness of change and improvement in social institutions and a growing conviction that man's early condition had been a savage one. Taking progress for granted, social scientists endeavored to discover its laws and stages. Auguste Comte, for example, set for "social physics" (or *sociology,* as he later called it) the task of discovering "by what necessary chain of successive transformations the human race, starting from a condition barely superior to that of a society of great apes, has been gradually led up to the present stage of European civilization." Like Rousseau, Comte regarded man as the only species of animal capable of evolution. The dynamic of human progress, he declared, was man's innate impulse to understand and control the world he lived in. Man's restless search for better understanding and control of the environment led him inevitably from a theological to a metaphysical to a positive, or scientific, way of thinking. Physics and chemistry had already reached the positive stage, and biology seemed on the verge of doing so. The establishment of sociology as the science of the whole process of historical development would cap the climax and usher in the final stage of social evolution. In that stage, scientists would constitute the new priesthood; Auguste Comte, no doubt, would be the patron saint of the new positivist order. Meanwhile, human nature would have been transformed by the gradual decay of aggressive and selfish impulses.

Karl Marx, too, developed a theory of social evolution

independently of theories of biological evolution. It was from the philosopher Georg Friedrich Hegel that Marx learned to view human history as a dialectical process involving thesis, antithesis, and synthesis. But whereas Hegel has conceived the process as essentially spiritual, Marx interpreted it "materialistically," that is, as an interaction between human nature and its changing social and natural environment. Primitive man, said Marx, sought unsuccessfully to control nature. Failing in this, he turned to subjugating his fellow man; thus he became the prisoner of social forces. Things, not ideas, molded the course of historical development. The mode of production determined the class structure and the ideological superstructure of society in every epoch. Progress occurred only when contradictions developed between the changing mode of production and the existing class structure. First the slave society of antiquity gave way to feudalism, then feudalism to capitalist enterprise. Capitalism, in turn, was destined to yield to a classless socialist society; human nature would be radically transformed by the elimination of private property. No longer enslaved by things, man would be free to shape his own destiny. Clearly Marx, like Comte, thought that history was going somewhere inexorably and that the historical process was ultimately redemptive of human nature. Social science was the study of the laws of historical development. It explained why and how change took place and indicated man's duty and destiny.

Not until we reach Herbert Spencer, whose first book appeared in 1850, do we find the idea of social evolution linked to the idea of organic evolution. Spencer was a staunch adherent of the free enterprise school of political economy founded by Adam Smith, Thomas Malthus, and David Ricardo. In essence he gave their doctrine an evolutionary and sociological twist, applying its concepts to the analysis of social evolution. According to Spencer, competition between individuals and races had provided the impetus to social progress from the earliest times. Primitive man had been wild and savage, as his barbarous condition required. Government was based on force and fear. In the course of time, however, population pressure precipitated a struggle for existence, placing a premium on ingenuity and capacity for voluntary co-operation. Some tribes and races responded to this challenge more effectively than others. These survived and carried forward the banner of progress. As human nature improved through competition, voluntary co-operation supplanted force and fear as the basis of social order. Eventually, said Spencer, human nature would be so transformed by competitive elimination that government would become unnecessary. Each individual would respect the rights of others as they respected his. All this would happen, of course, only if government gave a fair field to all and favors to none, so that competition could produce its beneficent effects. Thus, nine years before Darwin's *Origin of Species* appeared, Herbert Spencer made population pressure, struggle for existence, and survival of the fittest the key concepts in a theory of social evolution.

In biology Spencer was a Lamarckian rather than a Darwinian at this time. He had been converted to Lamarck's theory of evolution about 1840 by reading Charles Lyell's discussion of it in his *Principles of Geology*. Not until after Darwin had published his *Origin of Species* was Spencer able to proclaim a grand synthesis of biological and social theory in terms of universal competition and survival of the fittest. Adopting Darwin's explanation of biological progress, Spencer proceeded to draw the analogy to social progress:

> As with organic evolution, so with super-organic evolution. Though, taking the entire assemblage of societies, evolution may be held inevitable as an ultimate effect of the co-operating factors, intrinsic and extrinsic, acting on them all through indefinite periods of time; yet it cannot be held inevitable in each particular society, or even probable. A social organism, like an individual organism, undergoes modifications until it comes into equilibrium with environing conditions; and thereupon continues without further change of structure. When the conditions are changed meteorologically, or geologically, or by alterations in the Flora and Fauna, or by

migration consequent on pressure of population, or by flight before usurping races, some change of social structure is entailed. But this change does not necessarily imply advance. Often it is towards neither a higher nor a lower structure. Where the habitat entails modes of life that are inferior, some degradation results. Only occasionally is the new combination of factors such as to cause a change constituting a step in social evolution, and initiating a social type which spreads and supplants inferior social types. For with these super-organic aggregates, as with the organic aggregates, progression in some produces retrogression in others: the more-evolved societies drive the less-evolved societies into unfavourable habitats; and so entail on them decrease of size, or decay of structure.[2]

In Spencer's view, the progress of humanity had resulted from race conflict, from "a continuous over-running of the less powerful or less adapted by the more powerful or more adapted, a driving of inferior varieties into undesirable habitats, and, occasionally, an extermination of inferior varieties." Since progress had been generated in this way in the past, it would presumably continue to result from the same causes in the future, but Spencer drew back from this conclusion. The revival of militarism in Europe in the late nineteenth century alarmed him. The integration of simple groups into compound and doubly compound ones by military conquest had been carried "as far as seems either practicable or desirable," he declared. Progress in the future should result from "the quiet pressure of a spreading industrial civilization on a barbarism which slowly dwindles." But what if barbarism were to revive in the form of Prussian militarism, challenging the supremacy of British industrial civilization? Suppose it were to establish its claim to cultural and racial superiority by armed might? Would not this be progress, the survival of the fittest?

To these questions Spencer had no satisfactory answer. Having taken capacity to survive as the criterion of progress, he had no defense against the appeal to arms. He prized individual liberty above all things, but nature had little respect for freedom or individuality. If human history were but an extension of natural history, the prospects for individual liberty were dim and uncertain. Nazi race theory, not free enterprise, was the logical outcome of the biologizing of social theory.

Where did Darwin stand in relation to these developments? What was his contribution to the development of social science? Not the idea that human nature and institutions had developed through successive stages from brutish beginnings. That idea had been expressed off and on for over a hundred years, to say nothing of similar speculations in classical antiquity. Not the idea that the historical process was subject to laws of development. That had been the common assumption of nineteenth century social theorists. Not the idea that social evolution was a continuation of biological evolution. Herbert Spencer had propounded this thesis twenty years before Darwin published his views. Not even the idea that competition and natural selection had been responsible for the progress of civilization. Here, too, Spencer had staked out his claim in advance. Nevertheless, Darwin did make a contribution to social thought. In the first place, he threw the weight of his enormous prestige behind Spencer's idea that social progress had resulted chiefly, though not solely, from individual, tribal, and racial competition. Secondly, he converted the scientific community to the belief that early man was simply an anthropoid animal equipped with a better brain than his cousin anthropoids. This belief had been held by some social thinkers before Darwin, but it did not become a revolutionizing force in social thought until Darwin's work made it a basic postulate of modern social science.

It was precisely the necessity of showing as best he could how man's distinctively human traits might have originated without a special act of creation that forced Darwin to become a social scientist and social philosopher. As would be expected, he relied heavily on his theory of natural selection to account for both the intellectual and the moral progress of the human race. "I suppose that you do not doubt," he wrote to Charles

Lyell in 1859, "that the intellectual powers are as important for the welfare of each being as corporeal structure; if so, I can see no difficulty in the most intellectual individuals of a species being continually selected; and the intellect of the new species thus improved, aided probably by the effect of inherited mental exercise. I look at this process as now going on with the races of man; the less intellectual races being exterminated." [3]

Likewise with the moral sense. It was inevitable, said Darwin, that any gregarious animal reaching a certain stage of mental development should acquire a moral sense. Such an animal would become aware of the conflict between its individual impulses and the demands of the group. If it acted contrary to the demands of the group, it would feel a sense of shame and remorse, a sense of guilt. Once the moral sense had arisen in man's primitive ancestors, it would develop by natural selection.

A tribe including many members who, from possessing a high degree of the spirit of patriotism, fidelity, obedience, courage, and sympathy, were always ready to aid one another, and to sacrifice themselves for the common good, would be victorious over most other tribes; and this would be natural selection. At all times throughout the world tribes have supplanted other tribes; and as morality is one important element in their success, the standard of morality and the number of well-endowed men will thus everywhere tend to rise and increase. [4]

But Darwin was aware of the tendency in modern society to inhibit natural selection from exerting its full power.

With savages [he wrote], the weak in body or mind are soon eliminated; and those that survive commonly exhibit a vigorous state of health. We civilised men, on the other hand, do our utmost to check the process of elimination; we build asylums for the imbecile, the maimed, and the sick; we institute poor-laws; and our medical men exert their utmost skill to save the life of every one to the last moment. There is reason to believe that vaccination has preserved thousands, who from a weak constitution would formerly have succumbed to smallpox. Thus the weak members of civilised societies propagate their kind. No one who has attended to the breeding of domestic animals will doubt that this must be highly injurious to the race of man. It is surprising how soon a want of care, or care wrongly directed, leads to the degeneration of a domestic race, but excepting in the case of man himself, hardly any one is so ignorant as to allow his worst animals to breed.[5]

In passages like this, Darwin seemed to out-Spencer Spencer in emphasizing natural selection as the architect and agency of social progress. But he was not consistent in this point of view. Influenced either by his deep humanitarian feelings or his Christian upbringing or both, he noted that the agency of selection in developing the moral sense had been partially supplanted in modern times by "the effects of habit, the reasoning powers, instruction, religion, &c." As a result of these influences, said Darwin, a higher morality had developed, a morality that extended men's sympathies to "all races, to the imbecile, maimed, and other useless members of society, and finally to the lower animals." Not "every man for himself and the devil take the hindmost" but "do unto others as you would have them do unto you" had become the maxim of human conduct. "Looking to future generations," Darwin wrote, "there is no cause to fear that the social instinct will grow weaker, and we may expect that virtuous habits will grow stronger, becoming perhaps fixed by inheritance. In this case the struggle between our higher and lower impulses will be less severe, and virtue will be triumphant." [6]

This was most encouraging, but Darwin failed to note that he had become involved in a serious contradiction. If human sympathies became extended to all mankind, to all races and nations, to the imbecile and the maimed, what would become of the competitive struggle and hence of social progress? Darwin's "higher morality" would destroy the basis of social progress by inhibiting the elimination of the weak and unfortunate. Why, then, should it be called a "higher morality"? Why not a "lower morality" or a "higher immorality"? Thus Darwin, like Spencer, came face to face with the problem of the criteria of progress in a social science of historical development. Was progress to be defined simply as the production of more and more gifted breeds of men, "higher" in the sense of possessing superior faculties? Could one assume that a rise in intellectual endowment would be accompanied by a rise in morality? The connection was not self-evident. Moreover, what was the standard of morality to be? If the moral sense was nothing more than the voice of the tribe or other social group built into the individual by social training, how could there be general moral standards? Was not every group a law unto itself? Finally, there was the interesting question how religion could exercise a beneficial and refining influence on moral standards. In the new social science, religious beliefs and moral standards were regarded as forms of group adaptation to the environment. If there was a cosmic reality underlying religious behavior, the apprehension of that reality might possibly have a transforming effect on group mores. But Darwin recognized no such reality. He had, he wrote to a correspondent, an inward conviction that the universe was not the result of chance. "But then," he added, "with me the horrid doubt always arises whether the convictions of man's mind, which has been developed from the mind of lower animals, are of any value or at all trustworthy. Would any one trust in the convictions of a monkey's mind, if there are any convictions in such a mind?" [7]

Thus, Darwin and Spencer bequeathed to posterity the dream of an evolutionary social science, a science continuous with the science of biology, a science whose concepts were derived in large part from biology, a science that viewed man as distinguished from other animals chiefly, if not solely, by his superior intellectual powers. What has become of their dream in our own time?

Among modern biologists, especially the neo-Darwin-

ians, the hope of an evolutionary science of man and
society still burns bright. Like Herbert Spencer, Julian
Huxley envisages a comprehensive evolutionary science
embracing the history of the cosmos from its earliest beginnings in the dim recesses of time to its latest manifes-
tations in the evolution of man.

> Evolutionary science [Huxley writes] is a discipline
> or subject in its own right. But it is the joint product
> of a number of separate branches of study and learning.
> Biology provides its central and largest component, but
> it has also received indispensable contributions from
> pure physics and chemistry, cosmogony and geology
> among the natural sciences, and among human studies
> from history and social science, archaeology and pre-
> history, psychology and anthropology. As a result, the
> present is the first period in which we have been able
> to grasp that the universe is a process in time and to
> get a first glimpse of our true relation with it. We can
> see ourselves as history, and can see that history in its
> proper relation with the history of the universe as a
> whole.[8]

In working out this conception, however, the modern
Darwinians differ in various ways from their nineteenth-
century forebears. In the first place, they reject competition and conflict as agencies of social progress. They
point out that the term "fittest" in Spencer's expression
"survival of the fittest" is misleading if taken to imply
some substantive excellence in what survives. The surviv-
ing fittest, says Theodosius Dobzhansky, is simply the individual who has the most grandchildren. Julian Huxley
goes on to argue that competition within a species is
never a source of evolutionary advance. One suspects,
however, that the rejection of the Spencerian ideal of
competition by modern biologists and anthropologists
springs less from scientific certainties than from moral
revulsion against the uses to which this idea was put
by the Nazis. Selection by racial and national conflict
has proved too frightful in practice to be endured in
theory. Modern biologists prefer to minimize the role of

natural selection in human history and to treat mankind as a single unit undergoing progressive cultural evolution. For the same reason, they lay much greater stress on the uniqueness of man than Darwin's generation was prone to do.

> Man [says Theodosius Dobzhansky] is a zoological species. But this species has evolved properties so unique and unprecedented on the animal level that in man the biological evolution has transcended itself. Over and over again, some biologists made themselves ridiculous by urging solutions of human social and political problems based on the assumption that man is nothing but an animal. How dangerous may be such false keys to human riddles is shown by the fruits of one of these errors—the race theory.[9]

But when one asks in what the uniqueness of man consists, the difference between nineteenth and twentieth century evolutionary biology narrows again. The usual answer is that man is distinguished by his conceptual ability, hence by language, hence by the possession of a culture. Man is, so to speak, a culture-bearing, culture-transmitting animal. Here the matter is usually dropped, although it is sometimes noted in passing that man is subject to profound internal contradictions. The center of interest becomes, not an analysis of human nature, a subject barely mentioned at the recent Darwin centennial sessions in Chicago, but rather the discovery of the laws and processes of cultural evolution. On this subject, biologists are somewhat more cautious than they used to be. They make it perfectly clear that the transmission of culture through imitation and learning is decidedly different from the transmission of genotypes through biological reproduction, hence it forms the subject matter of a different science. They disclaim any intention to biologize social theory. On the other hand, they cannot resist the temptation to suggest a few analogies between biological evolution and cultural evolution.

The biologist [writes Julian Huxley] knows how fruitful has been the study of the mechanisms of genetic transmission for understanding the process of biological evolution. He can properly suggest to the humanist that a study of the mechanisms of cultural transmission will be equally fruitful for understanding the process of human history. Ideals, rituals, symbols, transmissible skills, beliefs, works of art—these seem to be the chief vehicles of this transmission. In addition to the self-reproduction and self-variation of material substance, in the shape of genes, we now have to consider the self-reproduction and self-variation of mental activities operating through the various media of cultural inheritance. Our analysis of biological evolution as a process has brought out a number of important facts and ideas—improvement, finite steps of advance, deployment, and the rest. The biologist knows that they will not be directly applicable in detail to cultural evolution, but he can be sure that they have their human analogies, and that equally important ideas will emerge from the study of human history as an over-all unitary process, ideas which will escape detection so long as history is treated merely as a record of separate sequences of events.[10]

Viewed in broad biological and historical perspective, Huxley suggests, human development will be seen to involve an initial movement of divergence of human races and cultures, followed by a movement of biological and cultural convergence. The latter process will reach fruition in the establishment of a world community. "It is easy enough to make broad statements about the steps of advance which have transformed the quality of human life and experience," Huxley adds. "What is difficult is to discover just how any one step is effected, still more to distinguish desirable from undesirable change, and restrictive from non-restrictive improvement. That is the job of the science of man." [11]

Not all biologists are as sanguine as Huxley concerning the possibility of understanding human development by analogy to biological evolution. Instead of attempting to canvass biological opinion in this matter, however, let us turn to the social scientists to whom modern biologists assign the task of erecting a science of culture. What has been the response among anthropologists to the demand for broad theories of cultural development? Generally speaking, contemporary anthropologists have had little to say on this subject. Early in the twentieth century a strong reaction set in against the social evolutionism of the previous century. This reaction was due partly to the shattering effect of world history on faith in progress, partly to dismay at the practical consequences of theories of racial conflict and supremacy, and partly to field research discrediting the idea that all societies pass through the same stages in their historical development. The cultural relativists stressed the uniqueness of the pattern of culture in each society and explained apparent instances of parallel evolution as results of cultural borrowing or independent invention. The functionalist school of anthropology has been even less interested in evolutionary problems.

But although evolutionary theories are scarce in contemporary anthropology, they are not completely absent. In the writings of the British prehistorian V. Gordon Childe and the American anthropologist Leslie White nineteenth-century social evolutionism lives on, but with Spencerian and Marxian ideas curiously blended. As we have seen, Marx was essentially Hegelian in his approach to history. He had little use for Darwin except as a stick with which to beat religion and philosophical idealism. His colleague Freidrich Engels, on the other hand, was profoundly influenced by Darwin. With Engels began the process of Darwinizing Marxian theory by emphasizing technology as the human animal's mode of adapting to the natural environment. This way of looking at society and culture is nicely illustrated in the writings of Childe and White, both of whom aspire to base a strictly objective, value-free social science on a biological-technological interpretation of history. Childe, for example, adopts population increase as his criterion of progress, stressing its objective, biological character. "Historical changes can be judged by the extent to which they have helped our species to survive and multiply," he writes.

Technology affords an equally objective criterion of progress:

> The shaduf, the Persian wheel, and the electric pump are not three instances of one species of water-raising appliance, but three species in an evolutionary hierarchy. The position of each in the series is given objectively by the efficiency with which it performs its recognized function, and this can be evaluated with mathematical precision.[12]

By this means, Childe concludes, the idea of progress can be vindicated against "sentimentalists and mystics."

Childe concedes, however, that historical and archaeological evidence fails to support the idea that every society or civilization progresses through pre-ordained stages. When contradictions develop between the mode of production and the social structure, progress does not always result. The society may become paralyzed or fossilized and fail to advance. Even when different societies in the same geographical region pass from barbarism to civilization, as in the ancient Middle East, the successive steps by which they make this transition do not exhibit even abstract parallelism. Instead, one sees a process of divergence followed by convergence through cultural borrowing and intermingling.

Nevertheless, Childe is not ready to give up the idea of progress or the analogy between social and biological evolution. He views the historical divergence of early Middle Eastern cultures as a process whereby a single rural economy became adapted to a variety of natural environments. Culture, he explains, is "the means by which societies adapt themselves to their environment so as to survive and multiply, taking the place of bodily modifications and instincts that serve animals to the same end." Progress occurs not so much in individual societies as in human culture as a whole. A particular society may become "over-specialized" (a favorite adjective among biologists) and so fail to progress, but its tools, customs, and ideas, if they offer some advantage to the human species, will be borrowed by other cultures. Thus, culture as a whole will advance indefinitely. New inventions, says Childe, are like biological mutations; they help societies to adapt to their environment. Among societies, as among organisms, there is a process of natural selection, not by war and battle (Childe is too good a Marxian to tolerate that) but by the survival and triumph of societies that foster the development of science, the march of invention, and the expansion of productive forces. But why should military conflict be excluded from this struggle for survival? Childe does not say. Only his aversion to war and his Marxian faith in the transformation of human nature through social revolution prevent his accepting the Spencerian conclusion toward which his argument presses.

Leslie White's interpretation of cultural evolution in terms of energy levels bears a close resemblance to Childe's theory. Culture, White tells us, is:

> . . . an elaborate mechanism, an organization of exosomatic ways and means employed by a particular animal species, man, in the struggle for existence and survival. . . . Everything—the cosmos, man, culture—may be described in terms of matter and energy. The primary function of culture is to harness and control energy so that it may be put to work in man's service.[13]

White then proceeds to trace the main stages of man's progress from the Old Stone Age to the present Power Age—"a fascinating story of adventure and progress of a species lifting itself up by its cultural bootstraps from the status of a mere animal to a radically new way of life, a way destined to win mastery over most other species and to exert a powerful and extensive control over the natural habitat." There is but one jarring note in White's paean of praise to the hero Technology. Nuclear technology, he warns, threatens to destroy civilization, "or at least to cripple it to such an extent that it might require a century, a thousand, or ten thousand, years to regain its present status."

> The belief and faith that civilization, won at such great cost in pain and labor, simply *cannot* go down in de-

struction because such an end would be too monstrous
and senseless, is but a naive and anthropocentric whim-
per. The cosmos does little know nor will it long remember what man has done here on this tiny planet.
The eventual extinction of the human race—for come it
will sometime—will not be the first time that a species
has died out. Nor will it be an event of very great
terrestrial significance.[14]

Cold comfort this, but White does not leave us entirely
without hope. Just possibly, he declares, there will emerge
from the next war a victor sufficiently powerful to or-
ganize the entire human species within a single social
system. "Then and only then will the curse of war be
lifted and the way made free and open for a fuller and
richer life."

Why the establishment of a single political state in the
world must eventuate in permanent peace and a more
abundant life for all mankind will not be immediately
apparent to those who have read and pondered Aldous
Huxley's *Brave New World* or George Orwell's *1984*. The
inveterate assumption underlying the gospel of progress
is the assumption that the growth of science and technology, of man's comprehension and mastery of nature,
will necessarily produce an increase in human happiness
and well-being. But is this true? Certainly there has been
progress of a sort in Western society and, over the long
view, for mankind as a whole. Life has become easier
for many. More people have opportunities to study, to
learn, to enjoy. Yet, strangely enough, man is not happy.
He wants to know whence he came, whither he is going,
and what he must do to find peace with himself and his
fellow man. His mind grows weary thinking of indefinite
progress onward and upward, of infinite future possibilities to be realized, when he is unable to realize a fraction
of the possibilities of his present nature.

And what are the possibilities of man's present nature?
We are told that we are animals but not ordinary animals. We have powers of thought and speech. We are
culture-transmitting animals. Our culture enables us to survive. But is culture nothing more than this? Socrates,

Sappho, Moses, Shakespeare, Newton, Einstein—were they engaged simply in enabling themselves and others to adjust to the environment? They thought there was more to it than that. For them the dignity of man consisted not in his power over nature but in his power to discover beauty, truth, and goodness. But these abstractions have no standing in White's science of culture.

The views of Childe and White should not be taken as typical of modern social science. They have been sharply criticized not only by anthropologists who are skeptical of social evolutionism generally but also by those who approach the problem of social evolution in a different way. There are, for example, the multi-linear evolutionists, led by Professor Julian H. Steward of the University of Illinois. In his *Theory of Culture Change,* published in 1955, Steward puts aside the search for laws governing the development of human culture as a whole. He calls, instead, for cross-cultural comparisons aimed at discovering and explaining the independent occurrence of similar cultural or institutional developments in different regions of the world—for example, the roughly similar stages of development of irrigation civilizations in the Far East, the Middle East, and in Meso-America. Postulating sequences of similar cultural constellations that succeed one another "in a regular and predetermined way because of developmental laws," Steward aims at discovering the causes of cultural change.

In developing his thesis, Steward explicitly rejects the idea that cultural evolution is an extension of biological evolution or that it has any necessary connection with "progress."

> We must conclude [he writes] that cultural evolution is not distinguished from cultural relativism or historical particularism by an essential similarity of its developmental scheme with that of biological evolution, by the characteristic of increasing complexity, or by the attribute of progress. This is not to say, however, that evolution lacks distinctive features. The methodology of [multilinear] evolution contains two vitally important assumptions. First, it postulates that genuine parallels of

form and function develop in historically independent
sequences of cultural traditions. Second, it explains
these parallels by the independent operation of identi-
cal causality in each case. . . . The methodology is
therefore avowedly scientific and generalizing rather
than historical and particularizing. It is less concerned
with unique and divergent (or convergent) patterns and
features of culture . . . than with parallels and similarities which recur cross-culturally. It endeavors to determine recurrent patterns and processes and to formulate
the interrelationships between phenomena in terms of
"laws." [15]

Steward's theory of social evolution differs from nineteenth century theories in its rejection of biological analogies, its lack of concern with the development of mankind as a whole, and its indifference to the idea of progress. But it retains the view that cultural developments
are subject to law and that adaptation to the environment
is an important determinant of social change. Cultural
ecology, Steward explains, "must supplement the usual
historical approach of anthropology in order to determine
the creative processes involved in the adaptation of culture to its environment." Historians of culture, observing
the variety of cultural patterns that develop in a single
environment, tend to conclude that environment is much
less important than the culture pattern itself. They con-
ceive this pattern as developing according to an inner
dynamic that defies scientific formulation. But this point
of view, says Steward, overlooks the ways in which modes
of adaptation to the environment condition cultural development.

Although technology and environment prescribe that
certain things must be done in certain ways if they are
to be done at all, the extent to which these activities
are functionally tied to other aspects of culture is a
purely empirical problem. . . . In the irrigation areas
of early civilizations . . . the sequence of socio-political
forms and culture cores seems to have been very similar
despite variation in many outward details or secondary
features of these cultures. If it can be established that

the productive arrangements permit great latitude in the socio-cultural type, then historical influences may explain the particular type found. The problem is the same in considering modern industrial civilizations. The question is whether industrialization allows such latitude that political democracy, communism, state socialism, and perhaps other forms are equally possible, so that strong historical influences, such as diffused ideology—e.g., propaganda—may supplant one type with another, or whether each type represents an adaptation which is specific to the area.[16]

From this passage it will be seen that Steward, although not an economic determinist, regards the mode of production (viewed as a method of adaptation to the physical environment) as a chief determinant of the "culture core" in any society, a determinant whose modifications shape the cultural development of the society. "Cultures do, of course, tend to perpetuate themselves," he writes. "But over the millennia cultures in different environments have changed tremendously, and these changes are basically traceable to new adaptations required by changing technology and productive arrangements." Thus, Steward's evolutionism is distinguished from that of Spencer, Marx, Childe, and White less by its view of man and his relation to nature than by its more modest pretensions. The biological frame of reference is discarded, but its influence lingers on.

Still another view of cultural evolution is that propounded by Alfred Louis Kroeber, whose death in 1960 marked the passing of the older generation of American anthropologists. In Kroeber's work, the historian and the natural historian jostle each other for supremacy. In the last edition of his famous textbook *Anthropology,* published in 1948, Kroeber claims the rank of a natural science for anthropology.

Man, to every anthropologist, is an animal in the given world of nature: that and nothing more—not an animal with a soul or immortality or destiny or anything else attached to him beforehand, but an animal to be compared, as to structure and as to function, on equal terms with other animals; and with the unshakable conviction that any special traits and qualities which may ultimately be assigned to him are to *eventuate from inquiry* instead of being presupposed. And, quite parallel, culture to every anthropologist is a set of phenomena that invariably occur in the world of nature wherever men appear in it—and essentially occur only there—and which again are to be studied comparatively, with complete equality of regard for all such phenomena, and without preappraisals among them. There is no room in anthropology for a shred of ethnocentricity, of homini-centricity; for prevaluations in favor of our civilization, our religion, our philosophy, our standards; nor room either for reservations of this product or that belief as being too noble or too fine to be studied by ordinary methods of natural science.

That is why, alone among what it is customary to call the social sciences, anthropology is recognized by astronomers, physicists, chemists, geologists, and biologists as a sister natural science—or at any rate as a potential one. Our accomplishments may not yet be as precise or as sure as theirs; but we are shooting at the same kind of marks in a similar way.[17]

Writing in this mood, Kroeber can match Herbert Spencer in developing analogies between culture and life, the superorganic and the organic. A culture is like a flora or a fauna. Culture areas resemble floral or faunal areas. A culture trait is like a species, a complex of culture traits like a genus or family. These complexes evolve like biological populations; the basic pattern endures but undergoes modification in special environments. Thus, alphabetic writing, plow agriculture, and Hebrew-Christian-Mohammedan monotheism began as pure inventions, "corresponding more or less to mutations or series of mutations in organic nature." In the course of time they spread into various cultures, becoming adapted to circumstances yet retaining their basic pattern.

Kroeber recognizes important differences between cultural evolution and organic evolution, however. He notes that basic cultural patterns are far less stable than the patterns conserved by heredity. They can coalesce as well as diverge and ramify. "The tree of life is eternally branching, and never doing anything fundamental but branching, except for the dying-away of branches. The tree of human history, on the contrary, is constantly branching and at the same time having its branches grow together again." [18] In historical development, Kroeber adds, the qualities of uniqueness and irreversibility, present to some degree in organic evolution, become predominant. Recorded history is "a series of objectively unique events whose major significance lies in their organization into distinctive patterns and not in ill-defined formulas or generalized denominators." [19]

Kroeber's anthropology presupposes a distinction between the historical and the scientific approach to the study of phenomena. The historical approach (whether applied to human history, earth history, or cosmic history) aims at descriptive integration. There is an imaginative reconstruction of the past in which the temporal and spatial relations and the qualitative flavor of events are preserved. Theories are validated by the general coherence they give to the events described. In science, on the contrary, the concrete connections of phenomena in space and time are ignored in a search for repetitive processes that can be tested quantitatively and experimentally. The laws thus discovered are relevant to historical reconstruction, but they are not themselves laws of historical development.

With this distinction between science and history Kroeber bids farewell to the long-cherished dream of a natural science of historical development, a dream that inspired many nineteenth-century social scientists and still inspires such writers as V. Gordon Childe and Leslie White.

If this dichotomous view is sound [writes Kroeber] there is no apparent room left for White's evolutionism as concerned with form-plus-sequence. The nonrepetitive parts of what he so designates, like the evolution of our universe, organic life, and human culture, are merely large histories. Other subjects in [White's] evolutionism, such as the growth of organic individuals

or radio-active deterioration, are repetitive and therefore are parts of the findings of science, in situations
in which sequence and duration happen to be unusually
conspicuous.[20]

Kroeber concedes that both the scientific and the historical approach are applicable in principle to all fields
of human inquiry. He observes, however, that the scientific approach has worked best on the inorganic level
"and decreasingly in the successively superposed ones."
Historical method, on the contrary, has been most suc-
cessful on the psycho-socio-cultural level. Thus, although
Kroeber does not completely abandon hope for an eventual science of culture (dealing presumably with repetitive cultural processes), he stresses the need for expand-
ing the use of historical method in anthropology. Even
repetitive processes, he declares, are unlikely to be discovered without historical research. Functionalist anthropologists dream of constructing a non-historical social
physiology from studies of existing societies and cultures,
but they forget that experiment and control, the essential
tools of the physiologist, are not available in the study
of man. To overcome this handicap, anthropologists
must resort to historical method. They must abandon their
exclusive preoccupation with non-literate societies and
avail themselves of the enormous wealth of material fur-
nished by the records of civilized history. Here alone,
says Kroeber, will they find sufficient data for the study
of cultural change.

Putting precept into practice, Kroeber produced his
monumental *Configurations of Culture Growth,* in which
he undertook to investigate "the frequent habit of societies
to develop their cultures to their highest levels spasmodic-
ally; especially in their intellectual and aesthetic aspects,
but also in more material respects." In this work, he puts
aside the question of the causes of cultural change, declaring that the anthropologist must discover *how* cultures
have behaved before attempting to explain *why.* From
Kroeber's other works it is plain, however, that he does
not restrict himself to technological, ecological, or economic interpretations of culture change. He discusses

changes produced by "the biological play impulse in its cultural expression," by restlessness and boredom, by religious experience and philosophical reflection, by cultural lag and social revolution. Far from being dismayed by the diversity of causes producing cultural change, Kroeber seems to revel in it. History, he declares, is "too richly varied" to be reduced to a simple succession of stages. [21]

Having brought the whole range of human history within the scope of anthropology, Kroeber has difficulty in maintaining the attitude of scientific objectivity he has prescribed for anthropologists. In the last edition of his *Anthropology*, the tension between Kroeber the natural scientist and Kroeber the humanist and historian is all too apparent. Anthropology is defined as "the science of groups of men and their behavior and productions," a science concerned with "generalized findings as to how culture operates" but also with "the major developments of the history of culture." The reader is warned that there is "no room for a shred of ethnocentricity or hominicentricity" in anthropology, yet he reads, no doubt with considerable pride and satisfaction, of man's "progress" and "advancement" in the Stone Age, of "richer" and "fuller" cultures contrasted to "thin and meager" ones, all viewed as parts of "the story of our collective human achievements."

As if sensing a certain homini-centricity in this language, Kroeber endeavors to define progress objectively. He undertakes to show that some levels of human culture are higher than others in "much the same way that a mammal is higher than an Ordovician sponge or brachiopod." But he is not content, like Childe, to adopt a purely biological criterion of progress, to regard man's ability to maintain himself in ever increasing numbers as proof of progress. He acknowledges the cumulative character of science and technology, but he also cites the decline of magic and superstitition and of "infantile obsession with the outstanding physiological events of human life" as evidence of progress.

All in all [he explains], retarded cultures seem infan-

tile both in their unabashed preoccupation with bodily
functions and in their disregard of other human lives
as compared with the gratifications of the ego. In this
sense, advanced cultures may be described as psycho-
logically more adult. Hence their unwillingness to interest themselves in personal physiology, but their concern about humaneness.[22]

Kroeber's vindication of progress, though less naive
than Childe's, is not as objective as he thinks. Doubtless
the facts are more or less as he represents them, but
the conclusion that these developments constitute progress involves some far-reaching value judgments. Childe
was content to take survival and the multiplication of the
human species as his criterion of progress (even this
criterion yields a dubious result in an atomic age), but
Kroeber obviously employs something more than a biological criterion. There is a hangover of the biological
point of view in his statement that songs, poems, and
philosophies are "pleasurable outlets for excess energy
rather than responses to actual needs," but he seems to
feel that poetry, philosophy, and science are worth-
while whether they have survival value or not. As for
"humaneness," why should one be concerned for mankind as a whole? Dogs are not concerned for the survival
or progress of dogkind. It may even be, if Darwin and
Spencer were right, that too much humaneness will re-
tard the progress of mankind by preserving the sickly,
the malformed, and the stupid at the expense of the
virile and intelligent. If so, why should increasing concern for man as man be a mark of progress?

It appears that Kroeber's resolution to view man and
other animals with equal regard has involved him in
contradictions and difficulties. Man turns out to have
some attributes a priori so far as his operations as anthropologist are concerned. These attributes are implicit
in the anthropological investigation itself. They do not
"eventuate from inquiry," at least not from scientific inquiry. Anthropological inquiry would be impossible if
man were not a rational animal capable of intellect and
science. Nor would it be undertaken if its value were not

presupposed. In such an inquiry, moreover, it is a fore-gone conclusion that magic and superstition will be re-garded as providing less insight into reality than scientific methods and that the growth of scientific attitudes will be viewed as constituting progress. Anthropology does not presuppose, however, that the anthropologist will value humaneness above the gratification of his own ego. If he does so value it, he will not do so as scientist. The dignity of man is not a scientific concept. Neither is progress, for at bottom it presupposes a vision of some potential harmony of man's nature, individual and social, which is valued for its own sake rather than for the sake of survival. Progress presupposes freedom and re-sponsibility, the actual efficacy of the ideal. It implies the spiritual unity of mankind, a form of unity unknown in other animal species.

The tensions implicit in the concept of scientific an-thropology are made the object of explicit analysis and reflection in the writings of Robert Redfield, author of the well-known classic *Folk Society*. Redfield sees two tensions or polarities in anthropological thought. On the one hand, the anthropologist is torn between the desire to consider man objectively as an animal sharing the characteristics of all life and the necessity to appreciate subjectively his distinctively human quality, "a quality not shared, or very little shared, with other forms of life." On the other hand, the anthropologist oscillates between an historical approach to human culture, in which the qualitative, spatial, and temporal connections among cul-tural phenomena are preserved, and a scientific approach, in which these connections are disregarded in a search for recurrent processes and generalized theories. In the nine-teenth century, says Redfield, anthropology was both his-torical and generalizing, taking culture-in-general and the evolution of culture-in-general as its subject. In the early twentieth century, interest shifted to the study of particular societies, mostly non-literate. The functional school of anthropologists attempted to develop an anat-omy and physiology of social and cultural systems. An-other school, looking to the humanities rather than to natural science for conceptual models, stressed the importance of total cultural pattern in determining social behavior. A third school examined the interaction of personality and culture, emphasizing the influence of typical life experiences on the genesis of individual and social character-structure. All three schools assumed that every society or culture was an organic whole, "an outgrowth of matter and life . . . subject to analysis by a relatively detached mind." Societies and cultures were "placed side by side, in timeless equivalence." The historical dimension of human culture was largely disregarded, but the drive toward scientific objectivity was counterbalanced in some degree by the effort to enter sympathetically into the mental universe of the peoples studied in order to understand their value systems, personality structure, and world view.

> The primitive culture or society [writes Redfield] is a complete world, a mental universe with its own special cast or character, and to begin to make the science you must come to live, in some measure, within such a world and see it from the inside out. To understand it so is an intensely human experience. To present it to others as a human whole is an act not unlike the work of the novelist or the historiographer. It is this fact, and not that moral and symbolic life is forbidden to science— which it is not—that makes our learning in a broad sense humanistic. Yet, although human wholes as humanly experienced by those who live within them are our subject matter, this subject matter can then be seen again by us from the outside, under the eye of universality in more abstract terms. And thus is science made of it.[23]

More recently, Redfield continues, anthropology has reacquired a broad historical perspective and an interest in a general human nature. This has come about primarily through the inclusion of peasant and rural societies and cultures within the scope of anthropological research. Whereas in 1923 the well-known British anthropologist A. R. Radcliffe-Brown restricted social anthropology to the study of non-literate peoples, by 1944 he was urging anthropologists to investigate civilized societies as well. Since that time field research on literate and preliterate peoples has begun to rival research on primitive tribes. This broadening of interest has affected the whole anthropological enterprise. When peasant societies in China, India, and South America are the object of research, it becomes impossible to ignore the historical dimension of culture. Once again anthropology comes face to face with the problem of cultural evolution, whether local, regional, or worldwide. "Once more our interest is both historical and generalizing," says Redfield. At the same time, the tension between the scientific and the historical-humanistic poles of anthropology is renewed and increased.

In one of his last books, *The Primitive World and Its Transformations,* Redfield takes up anew the problem of man's transition from a precivilized to a civilized condition. He recognizes the importance of the technological transformations described by V. Gordon Childe, but he doubts the adequacy of a purely technological interpretation of cultural evolution.

> The great transformations of humanity [writes Redfield] are only in part reported in terms of the revolutions in technology with resulting increases in the number of people living together. There have also occurred changes in the thinking and valuing of men which may also be called "radical and indeed revolutionary innovations." Like changes in the technical order, these changes in the intellectual and moral habits of men become themselves generative of far-reaching changes in the nature of human living. They do not reveal themselves in events as visible and particular as do material inventions, or even always as increasing complexity in the systems of social relationships. Nor is it perhaps possible to associate the moral transformations with limited periods of time as we can associate technological revolutions with particular spans of years. Yet the attempt to identify some of the transformations in men's minds can be made.[24]

Redfield's argument presupposes a distinction between

the technical order and the moral order in human societies. The moral order includes "all the binding together of men through implicit convictions as to what is right, through explicit ideals, or through similarities of conscience." The technical order includes "all the other forms of co-ordination of activity which appear in human societies."

> The technical order is that order which results from mutual usefulness, from deliberate coercion, or from mere utilization of the same means. In the technical order men are bound by things, or are themselves things. They are organized by necessity or expediency.[25]

The expansion of the technical order disintegrates the local moral orders in the regions where it develops, Redfield explains. But this process involves gain as well as loss. It paves the way for the development of new and more inclusive moral orders through the influence of "great ideas."

> Through civilization people are not only confused, or thrown into disbelief and a loss of will to live. Through civilization also people are stimulated to moral creativeness. Civilization is also ideas in history. It is new vision, fresh and bold insights, perceptions and teachings of religious and ethical truth which could not have come about had there not been expansion of the technical order which is the first and obvious aspect of civilization.[26]

Obviously, Redfield has come a long way from the view that man is simply an animal with a superior brain developing a variety of cultures in an effort to survive amid changing circumstances. Childe's treatment of ideas as "chiefly more or less adaptive to the technical (economic) order" seems totally inadequate to him. He speaks of "moral creativeness," "new vision," "fresh and bold insights," "perceptions and teachings of ethical and religious truth." By way of illustration he cites Plato's ideas and the monotheism of Ikhnaton, Judaism, and Christianity. He praises the great world religions as "the first great expansions of moral order to transcend the local community and the local culture and to embrace all humanity" and stresses the similar role played in modern times by ideas of permanent peace, a single world order, universal human responsibility, and universal human rights.

> Only civilization could bring about the circumstances of moral conflict in which these ideas could arise and the means for their transmission and reflective development. Civilization is a new dimension of human experience. The great idea, moving among many traditions and in newly troubled minds, is now an agent of change, a shaper of the moral order.[27]

This is all very inspiring, but it begs the question of the truth of the fresh insights and bold visions that shape and move history. Thereby it envelops the source of their creativity in mystery. It may be true, as Redfield suggests, that ideas are powerful in proportion as they are universally applicable. But the universality of an idea is no guarantee of its truth or of its ethical and religious creativity. Redfield begins by defining "moral order" in a purely descriptive way without raising the question of the validity of any specific moral order, but he does not hold this attitude consistently. As he describes the growth of wider and wider moral orders, he implies that the emerging new order is better and truer than the local moral orders left behind. The rise and progress of civilization then becomes a creative process in which the expansion of the technical aspect of human culture stimulates the spontaneous moral creativity of the human mind. The possibility that man may be averse to knowing and doing the good or that the vision of righteousness may come to him through an initiative not his own, overwhelming him with a sense of his own unworthiness, seems not to occur to Redfield. Moral creativity is assumed, not explained.

Redfield does, however, face the problem of the relativity of values in his last chapter, entitled "The Transformation of Ethical Judgment." Here he takes issue with Kroeber's dictum that anthropology has no room for any shred of ethnocentricity or homini-centricity. "My ethnocentricity," Redfield writes, "appears in the positive valuations I have placed on the increase and widening of humane standards, for are not such standards a special pride of Euro-American civilization? And my homini-centricity is patent: I have placed myself squarely on the side of mankind, and have not shamed to wish mankind well." Kroeber's dictum becomes difficult of application when one shifts from the study of primitive tribes to the study of Nazis, Russian communists, and Ku Kluxers, Redfield observes. Even in the case of primitive tribes, strict objectivity is not easy:

> It is that disturbing fellow, the living human individual, who makes trouble for the scientist's stern principle of perfect objectivity. Whenever the anthropologist looks at him, something human inside the anthropologist stirs and responds. It is easy enough to be objective toward objects; but the human individual refuses to be only an object. When he is there before you, he insists on being judged as human beings are judged in life, if not in science.[28]

This process of judging and valuing is inseparable from the anthropological inquiry, Redfield insists. Kroeber's evidences of genuine human progress presuppose civilized standards of truth and right. Civilized man judges the scientific and moral ideas and practices of primitive peoples by criteria he does not expect them to apply to him. In so doing, says Redfield, he recognizes that there has been a transformation of judgment with respect to both truth and right in man's passage to civilization. No civilized man really believes that the standards left behind are as good as those that have been acquired. Progress is no illusion. It is implied in the anthropological enterprise itself.

Redfield's *Primitive World and Its Transformations* shows clearly the complications that arise in anthropology once the spiritual dimension of man's nature is recognized. If ideas and ideals can be social forces in their own right, if they can be something more than expressions of class interest or libidinal drives, the anthropologist's search for laws and mechanisms of cultural change encounters serious difficulties. Moral insight, if it exists, is insight into some reality—into human nature as it is and as it may be, into man's total situation in the universe. If the doctrine of monotheism is creative, its creativity is presumably related to its truth. Or can false doctrines be creative? Merely to ask such questions is to reveal how unsusceptible they are of purely scientific answers. Their solution requires a philosophy of human nature and history. It presupposes a metaphysic. The idea of history or nature-history as a creative natural process is not a self-evident one. Science is relevant to it, but science cannot verify it.

Much of the difficulty in these matters arises from the perennial human tendency to fall into what Whitehead calls "the fallacy of misplaced concreteness." In the effort to deal with man by the methods of natural science we must perforce overlook those aspects of human nature and culture that do not readily lend themselves to formulation in scientific terms. We concentrate attention on those aspects of the subject matter that seem amenable to our method—man's animal organism, his social needs, and the stabilizing social influence of religious and moral beliefs. After a while we forget what we have left out. We begin to think we are looking at the whole reality. Culture becomes simply a mode of adaptation to the environment, morality simply a means of preserving social solidarity, religion nothing but a way of discharging individual and social tensions, and so on. This goes along very well until we are recalled to the concrete world by the necessity of action. Then we can no longer evade such questions as whether there are dimensions of reality inaccessible to science, whether some truths can be known only from the point of view of a responsible moral agent, whether religious beliefs relate to a reality that is more than social. If there are such truths, such dimensions of reality, the apprehension of them may be a cause of action. But how can science hope to calculate the influence of such causes on the total action situation?

The attempt of modern social science to avoid questions of this kind is fraught with danger. The danger arises from the fact that there is no neutral ground with respect to them. To suspend judgment is to decide for practical purposes that there are no such truths, no such dimensions of reality. The assertion that science can neither verify nor disprove them gives rise imperceptibly to a conviction that there is *no* way in which their validity can be tested. But where there are no tests of validity, there is no truth or falsity. There is only the bare fact of belief. If the ultimate ends of action have no basis in the structure of reality, there is little point to science. The passion for science then appears as an odd preference on the part of the scientist for a certain kind of activity. This is precisely the situation in which Darwin found himself at the end of his spiritual evolution. Science had become his passion, the only thing that made life bearable, but its ultimate significance was no longer clear to him. He was sure that he had been right in devoting his life to science, but he could not say why.

We conclude, then, that Darwin's influence on social thought has been a mixed one. Insofar as he opened a vast new perspective by showing man's organic relation to the animal kingdom, he took his place among the few greatest contributors to human knowledge. Insofar, however, as he reinforced Herbert Spencer's emphasis on individual, racial, and national competition as the source of social progress; insofar as he minimized the differences between man and other animals; insofar as he encouraged the idea that the methods of natural science are fully adequate to the study of human nature and society; insofar as he ignored the moral ambiguity of human progress and allowed himself to think that science could support itself without philosophy and religion; to this extent he contributed to the growth of misconceptions whose evil effects we still combat.

4

Conclusion

○

ONE WONDERS WHAT DARWIN WOULD HAVE TO SAY
if he could view the contemporary intellectual
scene. Doubtless he would be delighted with the progress
of evolutionary biology, especially the developments in
genetics, ecology, and human paleontology. In the last
of these he would be astonished at the bewildering array
of fossil hominids reaching back nearly a million years
into geological history. He would find the experts agreed
in postulating the animal origin of man's body but unable
to agree as to the precise line of descent. The British anthropologist Wilfrid E. Le Gros Clark would present him
with "a graded morphological series, arranged in an
ordered time sequence, linking *Homo sapiens* through
early Mousterian man, pre-Mousterian man, and small-
brained *Pithecanthropus*, with the still smaller-brained
Australopithecus," the whole series comprising "a remarkable confirmation of the connecting links postulated
and predicted by Darwin's hypothesis of the descent of
man." [1] At the same time, however, he would hear
Clark's collaborator Louis S. B. Leakey reject this picture of man's ancestry as "wholly contrary to known
facts and . . . at complete variance with what we know
happens in other animal groups." [2]

113

With respect to the origin of man's distinctively human attributes, Darwin would be disappointed to find matters little advanced beyond his own speculations in *The Descent of Man.* He would be discouraged to hear J. S. Weiner of the Anthropology Laboratory at Oxford University describe this subject as "one large baffling topic on which our evolutionary insight remains meagre." Equally disconcerting would be the testimony of the British neurologist Macdonald Critchley concerning the difficulties inherent in a purely Darwinian conception of the origin of language:

> It was implicit in this particular hypothesis as to evolution that differences between human and animal structure and function are matters of degree. Were this principle to be firmly established, then it would be difficult to avoid the idea that animal communication leads by insensible gradations to the faculty of speech in man. There are numerous linguistic objections to this view however. It is important to realise, too, that language does not stand alone in this matter and that there are other weighty considerations which lead to the well-nigh inescapable conclusion that some potent qualitative change occurs at a point somewhere between the anthropoid and *Homo sapiens.* . . . No "missing link" between animal and human communication has yet been identified.[3]

In the social sciences Darwin would encounter the greatest change of all. He would find evolutionary problems largely neglected and his own theory of social progress through natural selection in great disfavor. In the current emphasis on man's uniqueness as a culture-transmitting animal Darwin might sense a tendency to return to the pre-evolutionary idea of an absolute distinction between man and other animals.

In the wider field of philosophical and theological issues connected with evolution Darwin would find a situation familiar in general outline but novel in detail. At one end of the spectrum of opinion, he would discover religious fundamentalists like those of his own day, at the other end cosmic evolutionists seeking to comprehend the whole of reality in evolutionary terms in the manner of Herbert Spencer. Between these extremes he would encounter the various intermediate positions described in these pages, and many more besides. In the Christian world he would meet with concepts of revelation and inspiration unfamiliar to him, with new developments in biblical scholarship and interpretation, with varieties of natural theology quite different from Paley's design argument. Among professional philosophers he would find evolutionism no longer in vogue, abandoned to philosophically-minded astronomers and biologists, its place taken by existentialism and logical analysis. Above all, he would sense a deep moral and spiritual unrest, a profound questioning of much that his own generation took for granted.

How would Darwin react to this situation, so familiar yet so strange? Would he endorse the gospel of cosmic progress preached by Julian Huxley and others, or would he view it with the same suspicion and reserve he showed toward the cosmic evolutionism of Herbert Spencer and John Fiske? Would he still hold that the differences between man and other animals are differences of degree, capable of being explained by the theory of natural selection, or would he accept instead the view of the British ornithologist David Lack that "an essential part of human experience and human nature lies outside the terms of reference of science," and that "the claim for which Darwinism stands, that man has evolved wholly by natural means, is a philosophical and not a scientific claim"? [4] Would he abandon and repent his emphasis on individual and racial competition as the dynamic of social progress, or would he regard the contemporary aversion to this view as a soft-headed refusal to face facts? Would he still be hopeful of indefinite future progress in science, civilization, and morality, or would he share the cyclical view of his grandson Charles Galton Darwin, who, in his book *The Next Million Years,* holds out a Malthusian prospect of recurring periods of war, famine, and excess population alternating with occasional golden ages of artistic and intellectual achievement?

We cannot know what Darwin's thoughts would be if he could survey the course of ideas and events since he wrote, but we can state our own conclusion. Although Darwin contributed powerfully toward shaping the dominant world view of the twentieth century, he settled nothing in either philosophy or theology. This is not surprising in view of the relations between science and world view. Every great scientific synthesis stimulates efforts to view the whole of reality in its terms, and Darwin's theory of natural selection was no exception. But the views of reality that originate in this way are not themselves scientific, nor are they subject to scientific verification. They attempt to make sense not only of the facts "out there," held at arm's length by the observer, but also of the facts "in here," facts such as our awareness of our own act of existence, our appreciation of beauty, our sense of moral accountability, our communion with the source of being. Facts of the latter kind lie close to the heart of reality, but they do not lend themselves to scientific formulation. Attempts to explain them scientifically end by explaining them away. But science itself then becomes unintelligible. A scientist is a person seeking insight into the harmony of things. The harmony and the human spirit seeking to comprehend it are there first. They are pre-scientific. Darwin seems never to have grasped the implications of this fact. He had a profound intuition of the harmony of nature, of her "endless forms most beautiful and most wonderful," but he distrusted his intuitions. He distrusted them, his autobiography shows, because he feared that they could be explained scientifically as holdovers from man's animal past. Having doubted the reality of spirit, he suffered the spiritual consequences of his doubt. There is no escape from reality, least of all from spiritual reality. Insofar as our own world view, deriving from Darwin, Freud, Marx, Comte, and innumerable other sources, denies the reality of spirit, whether human or divine, we too must pay the price of that denial.

Notes

Chapter 1

[1] *The Autobiography of Charles Darwin 1809–1882 with Original Omissions Restored,* ed. Nora Barlow (New York: Harcourt Brace, 1959), 85–86.

[2] As quoted in *Rome and the Study of Scripture: A Collection of Papal Enactments on the Study of Holy Scripture together with the Decisions of the Biblical Commission* (St. Meinrad, Indiana: Grail Publications, 1958), 24.

[3] Archibald Alexander, *Evidences of the Authenticity, Inspiration, and Canonical Authority of the Holy Scriptures* (Philadelphia: Presbyterian Board of Publications, n.d.), 230.

[4] Matthew F. Maury to "My dear Sir," January 22, 1855, Maury Collection, Division of Manuscripts, Library of Congress, Washington, D. C.

[5] Richard Watson, *An Apology for the Bible . . .* (Dublin, 1796), 29.

[6] H. G. Wood, *Belief and Unbelief since 1850* (Cambridge, England: Cambridge University Press, 1955), 64 ff.

[7] Thomas Henry Huxley, *Science and Hebrew Tradition: Essays* (New York: Appleton, 1910), vii.

[8] Carroll Stuhlmueller, C. P., "Catholic Biblical Scholarship and College Theology," *The Thomist,* XXIII (October, 1960), 540–41. The decisions of the Biblical Commission may be found in *Rome and the Study of Scripture.*

[9] As quoted in Charles Hauret, *Beginnings: Genesis and Modern Science,* trans. E. P. Emmans (Dubuque, Iowa: The Priory Press, 1955), 78–79.

[10] Pope Pius XII, Encyclical Letter *Divino Afflante Spiritu,* translated in *Rome and the Study of Scripture,* 98.

[11] "A Response of the Biblical Commission to the Most Eminent Father, Archbishop Celestine Suhard . . . ," translated in *Rome and the Study of Scripture,* 150.

[12] As translated in *The Pope Speaks: The Teachings of Pope Pius XII,* ed. and comp. Michael Chinigo (New York: Pantheon, 1957), 245–46.

[13] As quoted in David M. Stanley, S. J., "The Concept of Biblical Inspiration," *Proceedings of the Twelfth Annual Convention of the Catholic Theological Society of America* (New York: Paulist Press, 1959), 70.

14 Stanley, "The Concept of Biblical Inspiration," *Proceedings of Twelfth Annual Convention,* 74.

15 Hauret, *Beginnings,* 57–58.

16 *Ibid.,* 76.

17 Count Henry Begouën, *Quelques souvenirs sur le mouvement des idées transformistes dans les milieux catholiques . . .* (Paris: Bloud & Gay, 1945).

18 J. T. Forestell, C. S. B., "The Limitation of Inerrancy," *Catholic Biblical Quarterly,* XX (1958), 17–18.

19 Lyman Abbott, *The Theology of an Evolutionist* (Boston and New York: Houghton Mifflin, 1897), 57.

20 *Evolution and Christian Thought Today,* ed. Russell L. Mixter (Grand Rapids, Michigan: William B. Eerdmans Publishing Co., 1959), 21.

21 *Ibid.,* 181.

22 Roland H. Bainton, "The Bible and the Reformation," *Five Essays on the Bible* (New York, 1960), 22; see also Paul Lehman, "The Reformers' Use of the Bible," *Theology Today,* III (October, 1946), 328–44; also, John Dillenberger, *Protestant Thought and Natural Science: A Historical Interpretation* (New York, 1960), Chap. i.

23 William Temple, *Nature, Man and God* (London: Macmillan, 1951), 317.

24 As quoted in John Baillie, *The Idea of Revelation in Recent Thought* (New York: Columbia University Press, 1956), 35.

25 Helmut Richard Neibuhr, *The Meaning of Revelation* (New York: Macmillan, 1952), 108.

Chapter 2

1 Isaac Newton, *Opticks . . .* (4th ed.; London, 1730), 376.

2 *The Autobiography of Charles Darwin 1809–1882 with Original Omissions Restored,* ed. Nora Barlow (New York: Harcourt Brace, 1959), 87.

3 Charles Darwin to Asa Gray, May 22, 1860, Down, quoted in *The Life and Letters of Charles Darwin Including an Autobiographical Chapter,* ed. Francis Darwin (3 vols.; New York: Appleton, 1898), II, 105.

4 Henry Ward Beecher, "The Two Revelations," in *Evolution and Religion* (Boston and Chicago: The Pilgrim Press, 1885), 44, 46.

5 Shailer Mathews and Others, *Contributions of Science to Religion* (New York and London: Appleton, 1925), 355, 358.

6 *Ibid.,* 376–77.

7 *Ibid.,* 383.

8 *Ibid.,* 421–22.

9 Douglas Horton, "Foreword," in Karl Barth, *The Word of*

God and the Word of Man (New York: Harper, 1957), 2–3.

[10] Reinhold Niebuhr, "The Truth in Myths," quoted in *Evolution and Religion: The Conflict between Science and Theology in Modern America,* ed. Gail Kennedy (Boston: Heath, 1957), 92.

[11] Barth, *The Word of God and the Word of Man,* 51–52.

[12] Karl Barth, *Dogmatics in Outline* (New York: Harper, 1959), 51.

[13] *Ibid.,* 52.

[14] *Ibid.,* 59.

[15] Emil Brunner, "Nature and Grace," in *Natural Theology, Comprising "Nature and Grace" by Professor Dr. Emil Brunner and the Reply "No!" by Dr. Karl Barth,* trans. Peter Fraenkel (London: Geoffrey Bles: The Centenary Press, 1946), 32–33.

[16] *Ibid.,* 58.

[17] Reinhold Niebuhr, "The Truth in Myths," *Evolution and Religion,* 96.

[18] Helmut Richard Niebuhr, *The Meaning of Revelation* (New York: Macmillan, 1952), 172–73.

[19] Paul Tillich, "Natural and Revealed Religion," *Christendom,* I (October, 1935), 169.

[20] Maurice R. Holloway, S. J., *An Introduction to Natural Theology* (New York: Appleton-Century-Crofts, 1959), 144.

[21] Étienne Gilson, *God and Philosophy* (New Haven: Yale University Press, 1941), 126–27, 130.

[22] Raymond J. Nogar, O. P., "The Darwin Centennial: A Philosophical Intrusion," *The New Scholasticism,* XXXIII (October, 1959), 437.

[23] *Ibid.,* 443–44.

[24] J. Roland E. Ramirez, "The Ultimate Why of Evolution," *The New Scholasticism,* XXXIII (October, 1959), 476, 478.

[25] *Ibid.,* 480–82.

[26] Frederick Temple, *The Relations of Religion and Science* (London, 1884), 122–23.

[27] *Ibid.,* 230–31.

[28] William Temple, *Nature, Man and God* (London: Macmillan, 1951), 129; original edition in 1934.

[29] *Ibid.,* 263.

[30] *Ibid.,* 301.

[31] Julian Huxley, *Evolution in Action* (New American Library of World Literature [New York: Harper & Brothers, 1957]), 11–12. Reprinted by permission of Harper & Brothers.

[32] *Ibid.,* 47–48.

[33] *Ibid.,* 101.

[34] *Ibid.,* 109.

[35] *Ibid.,* 31.

[36] Theodosius Dobzhansky, "Evolution at Work," *Science,* CXXVIII (May 9, 1958), 1096.

[37] Ronald A. Fisher, *Creative Aspects of Natural Law* (Cambridge, England: Cambridge University Press, 1950), 18.

38 Thomas Henry Huxley, *Man's Place in Nature and Other Anthropological Essays* (New York, 1898), 151.

39 L. C. Birch, "Creation and the Creator," *Journal of Religion,* XXXVIII (April, 1957), 90–91.

40 Pierre Teilhard de Chardin, S. J., *The Phenomenon of Man* (New York: Harper, 1959), 306.

41 Bruno de Solages, "Christianity and Evolution," *Cross Currents,* I (Summer, 1951), 35. This article is highly recommended by Father Franklin J. Ewing, S. J., in "Human Evolution–1956—with Appendix on 'The Present Catholic Attitude Towards Evolution,' " *Anthropological Quarterly,* XXIX (October, 1956), 133.

42 Raymond J. Nogar, O. P., "The Paradox of the Phenomenon," *Dominicana,* XLV (Fall, 1960), 248–49.

43 James Collins, "Darwin's Impact on Philosophy," *Thought,* XXXIV (Summer, 1959), 185–248; James Street Fulton, "Philosophical Adventures of the Idea of Evolution: 1859–1959," *The Rice Institute Pamphlet,* XLVI (April, 1959), 1–31.

Chapter 3

1 Arthur O. Lovejoy, "The Supposed Primitivism of Rousseau's Discourse on Inequality," in *Essays in the History of Ideas* (Baltimore, 1948), 36; see also John C. Greene, *The Death of Adam: Evolution and Its Impact on Western Thought* (Ames, Iowa: Iowa State University Press, 1959), Chap. vii.

2 Herbert Spencer, The Principles of Sociology (New York: Appleton, 1877), 106–108.

3 Charles Darwin to Charles Lyell, October 11, 1859, Ilkley, Yorkshire, in *The Life and Letters of Charles Darwin Including an Autobiographical Chapter,* ed. Francis Darwin (3 vols.; New York: Appleton, 1898), II, 7.

4 Charles Darwin, *The Descent of Man, and Selection in Relation to Sex* (New York: Appleton, 1886), 132.

5 *Ibid.,* 133–34.

6 *Ibid.,* 125.

7 Charles Darwin to William Graham, July 3, 1881, Down, in *Life and Letters,* I, 285.

8 Julian Huxley, *Evolution in Action* (New York: Harper & Brothers, 1957), 9. Reprinted by permission of Harper & Brothers.

9 Theodosius Dobzhansky, "Human Nature as a Product of Evolution," in *New Knowledge in Human Values,* ed. A. H. Maslow (New York: Harper & Brothers, 1959), 75.

10 Huxley, *Evolution in Action,* 119. Reprinted by permission of Harper & Brothers.

11 *Ibid.,* 124–25. Reprinted by permission of Harper & Brothers.

12 V. Gordon Childe, *What Is History?* (New York: Schuman, 1953), 64; see also Childe's *Man Makes Himself* (New York:

Mentor, 1951) and his *Social Evolution* (New York: Schuman, 1951), Chap. xii.

13 Leslie White, *The Science of Culture* (New York: Farrar, Straus, 1949), 363.

14 *Ibid.*, 391.

15 Julian H. Steward, *Theory of Culture Change* (Urbana, Illinois: University of Illinois Press, 1955), 14.

16 *Ibid.*, 41–42.

17 A. L. Kroeber, *Anthropology* (New York: Harcourt Brace, 1948), 841.

18 A. L. Kroeber, "Structure, Function, and Pattern in Biology and Anthropology," in *The Nature of Culture* (Chicago: University of Chicago Press, 1952), 86.

19 *Ibid.*, 86.

20 A. L. Kroeber, "History and Evolution," *Southwestern Journal of Anthropology*, II (1946), 13–14.

21 A. L. Kroeber, *Configurations of Culture Growth* (Berkeley and Los Angeles: University of California Press, 1944); see also his *Anthropology*, Chap. x.

22 Kroeber, *Anthropology*, 301.

23 Robert Redfield, "Societies and Cultures as Natural Systems," *Journal of the Royal Anthropological Society of Great Britain and Ireland*, LXXXV (1955), 20; see also his "Relations of Anthropology to the Social Sciences and to the Humanities," in *Anthropology Today: An Encyclopedic Inventory* (Chicago: University of Chicago Press, 1953).

24 Robert Redfield, *The Primitive World and Its Transformations* (Ithaca, New York: Cornell University Press, 1953), 24–25.

25 *Ibid.*, 20–21.

26 *Ibid.*, 77.

27 *Ibid.*, 80–82.

28 *Ibid.*, 145, 151–52.

Chapter 4

1 Wilfrid E. Le Gros Clark, "The Crucial Evidence for Human Evolution," *Proceedings of the American Philosophical Society*, CIII (April, 1959), 171.

2 Louis S. B. Leakey, "The Origin of the Genus *Homo*," in *Evolution After Darwin: The Evolution of Man*, ed. Sol Tax (Chicago: University of Chicago Press, 1960), 29.

3 Macdonald Critchley, "The Evolution of Man's Capacity for Language," in *Evolution After Darwin*, 307; J. S. Weiner, "Physical Anthropology: An Appraisal," in *Evolution and Anthropology: A Centennial Appraisal* (Washington, D. C.: Anthropological Society of Washington, 1959), 34.

4 David Lack, *Evolutionary Theory and Christian Belief: The Unresolved Conflict* (London: Methuen, 1957), 105–106.

Index

The Mentor Philosophers

The entire range of Western speculative thinking from the Middle Ages to modern times is presented in this series of six volumes. Each book contains the basic writings of the leading philosophers of each age, with introductions and commentary by noted authorities.

"A very important and interesting series."
—*Gilbert Highet*

75 cents each

THE AGE OF BELIEF: The Medieval Philosophers *edited by Anne Fremantle.* (#MT463)
"Highly commendable . . . provides an excellent beginning volume." —*The Classical Bulletin*

THE AGE OF ADVENTURE: The Renaissance Philosophers *edited by Giorgio de Santillana.* (#MT437)
"The most exciting and varied in the series."
—*New York Times*

THE AGE OF REASON: The 17th Century Philosophers *edited by Stuart Hampshire.* (#MT367)
"His (Hampshire's) book is a most satisfactory addition to an excellent series." —*Saturday Review*

THE AGE OF ENLIGHTENMENT: The 18th Century Philosophers *edited by Sir Isaiah Berlin.* (#MT473)
"(Sir Isaiah) has one of the liveliest and most stimulating minds among contemporary philosophers."
—*N. Y. Herald Tribune*

THE AGE OF IDEOLOGY: The 19th Century Philosophers *edited by Henry D. Aiken.* (#MT421)
". . . perhaps the most distinct intellectual contribution made in the series." —*New York Times*

THE AGE OF ANALYSIS: 20th Century Philosophers *edited by Morton White.* (#MT353)
"No other book remotely rivals this as the best-available introduction to 20th century philosophy."
—*N. Y. Herald Tribune*